UNIVERSITY
MATHEMATICAL TEXTS

Founded by A. C. Aitken
and D. E. Rutherford

Editors:
ALAN JEFFREY
IAIN T. ADAMSON

20

TOPOLOGY

RECENT
UNIVERSITY
MATHEMATICAL
TEXTS

*The complete list of titles in the
series may be obtained from the Publishers*

TOPOLOGY

E. M. PATTERSON

Professor of Mathematics
University of Aberdeen

OLIVER & BOYD

EDINBURGH

INTERSCIENCE PUBLISHERS INC.
NEW YORK
A division of John Wiley & Sons Inc.

OLIVER AND BOYD LTD
Tweeddale Court,
Edinburgh 1

05 001336 X
First published 1956
Second Edition 1959
Reprinted 1963
Reprinted 1969
© 1969 E. M. Patterson
All rights reserved

Printed in Great Britain by
John Dickens & Co. Ltd., Northampton

PREFACE

Topology is now included in Honours Courses in Mathematics in most Universities. This book is designed to meet the needs of students taking such a course, and others who wish to become familiar with the basic ideas and methods. Its aim is to introduce the reader to the new ideas gradually. For example, the concept of a topological space is approached through a study of continuity in Euclidean spaces and then metric spaces. Abstract or general definitions are delayed until the reader is likely to be in a position to appreciate their significance.

I have tried to avoid introducing long and difficult proofs which might distract the reader's attention from the development of the theory. In giving proofs, I have included details which might be omitted in a more advanced treatise, preferring to sacrifice brevity to intelligibility. I have also avoided those sections of modern topology which seem too deep for a beginner to appreciate.

The book can be regarded essentially as an introduction to topology, and it is hoped that the interested reader will gain from it sufficient knowledge to enable him to proceed to more advanced treatises with confidence. I have, therefore, endeavoured to use standard definitions, notations and terminology throughout; but there are various different conventions adopted in the existing literature and I have not always found it easy to decide which authors to follow.

I owe much to the works listed in the bibliography, all of which I have consulted in the preparation of this book. Perhaps the most influential of these was M.H.A.Newman's "Elements of the Topology of Plane Sets of Points", which

I studied in some detail in co-operation with Dr.D.Borwein of St. Andrews University. However, the ground covered by Professor Newman is essentially different from the ground covered in this book.

I am grateful to all my friends who have shown an interest in this book, in particular to Dr. A. H. Read of St. Andrews University, who read and criticised the manuscript, and to Dr. Barbara Maitland of Liverpool University, who read the proofs and made several useful suggestions. I am especially grateful to Dr. D. E. Rutherford, who suggested the book in the first place, kept it alive, and assisted through all its stages, showing great patience at all times. Finally, I should like to thank the Publishers and Printers for their courtesy and co-operation, and in particular for their useful suggestions concerning the illustrations.

St. Andrews,   E. M. Patterson
    November, 1955.

PREFACE TO THE SECOND EDITION

I am indebted to many friends and colleagues who have drawn my attention to errors and misprints in the first edition, and who have made suggestions for improvements. No substantial changes have been incorporated in this new edition.

Leeds,   E. M. Patterson
    April, 1959.

CONTENTS

CONTENTS

CHAPTER IV

HOMOTOPY

CHAPTER V

SIMPLICIAL COMPLEXES

CHAPTER VI

HOMOLOGY

CHAPTER I

INTRODUCTION

The word **topology** is derived from the Greek word τόπος, meaning 'a place'. In mathematics topology was formerly defined to be the study of situation; an alternative name was **analysis situs.** The subject arose as a branch of geometry, but in recent years it has been generalised to such an extent that it has become involved with many other branches of mathematics. Nowadays mathematicians are in fairly general agreement that topology is a study of continuity. Since continuity plays an important part in mathematical analysis, it is not surprising that topology has come under the influence of the rigorous discipline of that subject. One result of this is that modern topology, if presented formally without preliminary discussion, is a difficult subject for the beginner. In an attempt to overcome this difficulty, the first chapter of this book is devoted to a descriptive account of the basic ideas of topology. This should help to provide motives for the discussions in the subsequent chapters. No attempt to be rigorous is made until Chapter II.

1. Topological Equivalence. An important section of elementary Euclidean geometry deals with the congruence of triangles and other figures. Congruence is a type of equivalence between geometrical figures; it expresses the fact that two figures are identical except for position in space. Similarity is another type of equivalence encountered in elementary Euclidean geometry. Figures which are similar are of the same shape, but are not necessarily of the same size. Similarity is a weaker form of equivalence than congruence, for congruent figures are necessarily similar, but similar figures need not be congruent. In projective geometry, an entirely different form of equivalence, based on the notion of perspective, plays a fundamental rôle. In this case, the shapes and sizes of equivalent figures need not be the same, but the figures do possess certain common properties; for example a straight line in one figure corresponds to a straight line in an equivalent figure.

The fundamental type of equivalence in topology is called **topological equivalence** or **homeomorphism.** Two geometrical figures are topologically equivalent, or homeomorphic, if each can be transformed into the other by a continuous deformation. For example, if a piece of plasticine is moulded into various different shapes without making breaks or joins, then all the associated geometrical figures are topologically equivalent. Thus the surfaces of a sphere, an ellipsoid, a cube and a tetrahedron are all topologically equivalent, but none of these figures is topologically equivalent to the surface of a torus (a figure shaped like an anchor-ring or a doughnut).

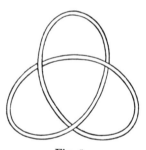

Fig. 1

Topology is concerned mainly with intrinsic properties of figures, that is to say properties of the figures themselves, and not properties concerning their relationship to any surrounding space in which they may be imbedded.

The experiments described in the previous paragraph are performed in physical space, which plays an essential part, and so they give an incomplete picture of the idea of topological equivalence. For example, whilst it is not possible to give a practical demonstration of deforming continuously a knot of the type shown in figure 1 into a circle, the two are nevertheless topologically equivalent. In a four-dimensional space, this knot could be deformed continuously into a circle.

2. Surfaces. To illustrate some of the ideas encountered in topology, we shall consider certain surfaces. Familiar surfaces in elementary three-dimensional geometry are the sphere, the circular cylinder, the circular cone, the ellipsoid, the hyperboloid of one or two sheets and the paraboloids. Since all spheres are homeomorphic, we speak of *the* sphere rather than *a* sphere; we are, in fact, really considering a class of surfaces all homeomorphic with a given sphere and using one particular member of this class as a representative. A similar convention is adopted for other surfaces.

Less familiar surfaces are the torus, the double-torus and the general n-fold torus of which these two surfaces are particular examples. The torus is represented in figure 2. The n-fold torus is a similar surface, but it has n holes instead of one.

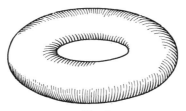

Fig. 2

The cylinder and the torus can be constructed by joining together opposite edges of a rectangle, a process which is known as identification. Let $ABCD$ be a rectangle and join

together *AB* and *CD* in such a way that *A* coincides with
D and *B* with *C*, as illustrated in figure 3. The resulting

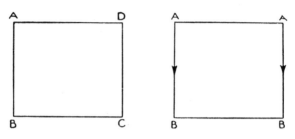

Fig. 3

surface is a finite cylinder. It is represented by a rectangle
with two opposite edges identified. The arrows on these
edges indicate that they have been joined together directly,
as shown in figure 4.

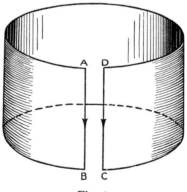

Fig. 4

Further direct identification of the two remaining edges
of the original rectangle produces the torus. The appropriate diagrams for this identification are shown in figure 5.

The actual construction from the rectangle is indicated in figure 6.

Fig. 5

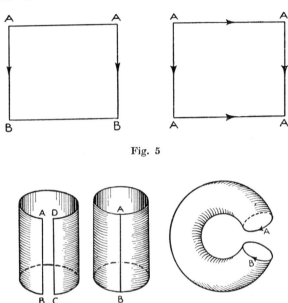

Fig. 6

Starting with the same rectangle $ABCD$, we can obtain other surfaces by using a different type of identification. If we identify AB and CD in such a way that A coincides with C and B with D, we obtain a surface known as the **Möbius band.** In this case the sides AB and CD are identified in the opposite sense, so that the arrows on the second diagram in figure 7 are in opposite directions. The reader is recommended to construct a model of the Möbius band by twisting one end of a rectangular piece of paper through 180° and gumming it to the other end. The resulting surface is shown in figure 8.

Topologically the Möbius band is a different surface from the cylinder, which means that the two surfaces are not homeomorphic. This can be seen by constructing paper

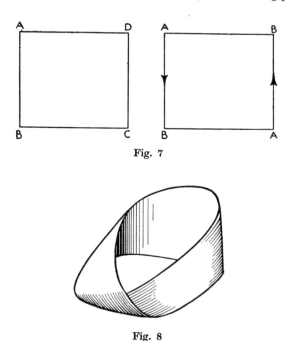

Fig. 7

Fig. 8

models of the two surfaces by the processes just described, and then cutting each along the line which originally joined the mid-points of the sides *AB* and *CD* of the rectangle. One complete cut divides the cylinder into two portions, but leaves a single piece of paper in the case of the Möbius band. This piece of paper has two twists in it, and it is in fact, homeomorphic to the cylinder; but this property cannot be demonstrated by a physical experiment.

Further identification of the sides of the original rectangle

if carried out as indicated in figure 9, produces a surface
known as the **Klein bottle.** The identification in this case
is a direct one, but it is impossible to construct a model

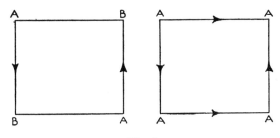

Fig. 9

of the Klein bottle in physical space without self-inter-
sections; the surface must cross over itself somewhere.
This self-intersection property is not an intrinsic property
of the Klein bottle; if a construction in a four-dimensional
space were possible, it need not occur.

In the above construction of the Klein bottle the opposite
pairs of edges of a rectangle were identified, one pair
directly and the other pair in opposite senses. If both pairs

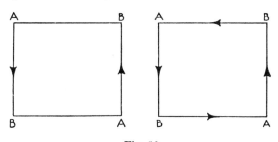

Fig. 10

of edges are identified in opposite senses, the resulting
surface is known as the **real projective plane.** The construction is indicated in figure 10. It is to be observed that,

in the final diagram, there are two distinct vertices, whereas in the diagrams representing the torus and the Klein bottle there is only one.

The real projective plane can be represented in various ways. The usual definition is as follows. Let P be any point of three-dimensional Euclidean space. Then any straight line through P is called a point of the real projective plane, and the real projective plane itself is the collection of all such points. Since any sphere of centre P meets a straight line through P in exactly two points, which are diametrically opposite, the real projective plane can be regarded as the surface obtained when diametrically opposite points of the surface of the sphere are identified. To obtain the representation given in figure 10, we consider one hemisphere and the equator. Each point on the hemisphere but not on the equator represents uniquely one point on the real projective plane; replacing such a point on the hemisphere by the foot of the perpendicular from the point to the plane of the equator, we obtain a representation in which the real projective plane is regarded as consisting of the points on and interior to a circle, with diametrically opposite points on the circumference identified. This is essentially the same representation as in figure 10; the circle has been replaced by a rectangle, but this is immaterial.

The surfaces described in this section are very special examples of the spaces considered in topology. In Chapter II we shall consider the general **topological spaces,** for which geometrical pictures such as the above are not always available.

3. Two-sidedness and Orientability. Surfaces can be either two-sided or one-sided. The sphere, the cylinder and the torus are examples of two-sided surfaces; they have both an 'inside' and an 'outside'. The physical idea of a two-sided surface is that it is one for which points on one side cannot be joined to points on the other by a continuous curve which does not cross any bounding part of the surface. For example, a continuous curve joining a point on the inside of the cylinder to a point on the outside must either pass through the surface of the cylinder itself or cross over the boundary at one of the ends.

The Möbius band, the Klein bottle and the real projective plane are examples of one-sided surfaces. On these it is not possible to distinguish between inside and outside. For example, any point on a paper model of the Möbius band, whose construction was described in § 2, can be joined to any other point by means of a continuous pencil line which does not leave the paper or cross over the edge.

The idea of **orientability** is derived from the physical idea of two-sidedness. Suppose that, around each point of a surface (except for points of the boundary, if there is one), a small closed curve is drawn, with a definite sense — either clockwise or anti-clockwise — attached to it. Then the surface is said to be **orientable** if it is possible to choose the senses so that they are the same for all points sufficiently near to one another. Otherwise the surface is said to be **non-orientable.**

It is easily seen that a one-sided surface is non-orientable. For example, the line joining the mid-points of the sides AB and CD of the rectangle $ABCD$ of figure 7 becomes a closed curve when the figure is changed into a Möbius band, and no point of this curve is on the boundary of the surface. It is impossible to draw a circle round each point of this curve so that no two neighbouring circles have opposite senses. This is most easily seen by picturing the circle round a particular point being moved along the curve. By the time it returns to its original position, its sense has been reversed.

It can also be shown that if a surface is two-sided in the physical sense already described, then it is orientable.

4. Connection. Most of the surfaces encountered in elementary geometry are connected, which is usually taken to mean that any two points on such a surface can be joined by a continuous curve; in topology a space satisfying this property is said to be **arc-wise connected.** An example of a surface which is not connected is the hyperboloid of two sheets. Disconnected surfaces are, in many cases, really only combinations of two or more distinct connected surfaces, and there is usually no loss in generality, for surfaces encountered in elementary geometry, in considering only connected surfaces.

There are, however, different kinds of connection. Consider, for example, an ordinary closed curve on the surface of the sphere. Such a curve can be contracted continuously into a point without leaving the surface. This may not be

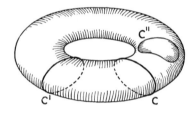

Fig. 11

possible on the surface of the torus; for example the circle C shown in figure 11 cannot be contracted continuously into a point without leaving the surface of the torus. A connected surface for which every ordinary closed curve can be contracted continuously into a point without leaving the surface is called **simply connected.** Thus the sphere is simply connected, but the torus is not.

A similar property which distinguishes simply connected from non-simply connected surfaces is that on the former any simple closed curve can be deformed continuously into any other, but this is not true on the latter. This is the basic idea behind the concept of **homotopy;** a curve which can be deformed continuously into another is said to be homotopic to it. In figure 11, C is homotopic to C' on the surface of the torus, but C is not homotopic to C''. Homotopy plays an important part in modern topology.

The Jordan curve theorem provides another illustration of the different types of connection of the surfaces of the sphere and the torus. Any curve homeomorphic to a circle is called a Jordan curve; the closed curves in the above illustrations are all Jordan curves. The theorem states that, on the plane and the sphere, such a curve divides the surface into two distinct regions, which have no point in common but which have the given curve as a common boundary. Clearly this is not true for the torus.

The Jordan curve theorem seems at first sight to be trivial, since it embodies a property which physically is more or less obvious. However, appearances in topology are sometimes deceptive, and the theorem, like many others which appear to be obvious, is difficult to prove.

5. Topological invariants. Classification problems are important in many branches of mathematics. In topology, the main problem is to collect together topological spaces into sets such that all spaces in a given set are topologically equivalent. One way of characterising these sets is to associate with the spaces certain entities (frequently numbers or groups) which are essentially the same for all spaces in a given set. Such entities are called topological invariants, because they are the same for all topologically equivalent spaces. Certain invariants may be equal for non-equivalent spaces; a complete classification is achieved only when no two different sets have all their invariants equal.

This classification problem has been of considerable interest ever since topology was first studied seriously (by the French mathematician Poincaré) and it is still the goal of much present-day research. The problem has been solved completely for compact two-dimensional manifolds: that is, ordinary closed bounded two-dimensional surfaces without edges, such as the sphere, the torus, the Klein bottle and the real projective plane. In particular it has been shown that every orientable compact two-dimensional manifold is homeomorphic to a sphere or an m-fold torus for some integer m; non-orientable compact two-dimensional manifolds can be classified in a similar manner. For more complicated spaces the classification problem has not been solved. Many topological invariants have been found, but in the general case no set has yet been discovered which has been proved to be sufficient to ensure that two spaces with the same invariants are necessarily topologically equivalent.

6. Euler's theorem on polyhedra. An example of a topological invariant occurs in Euler's theorem on polyhedra which states that, if F is the number of faces, E the number of edges and V the number of vertices of a polyhedron, then $F - E + V = 2$. The invariant here is $F - E + V$; its value for ordinary polyhedra is 2. A generalisation of the theorem brings out the invariant character more clearly. This states that, if any closed surface is divided into F regions by means of E arcs, joining, in pairs, V vertices such that at least two edges meet at each vertex, then the expression $F - E + V$ is independent of the method of dividing up the surface.

To prove this theorem, we first observe that, given any two divisions of the surface into faces, edges and vertices, a third division can be constructed so as to contain all the faces, edges and vertices of both the original divisions. This is done by adding new vertices at points of intersection of the edges of the two systems; this process introduces new edges and new faces. All we need to prove now is that, for any division obtained from a given one by adding new vertices, edges and faces the value of $F - E + V$ is the same. Suppose that one new vertex is added, and that this vertex is joined to some of the existing vertices by n new edges. This increases the number of faces by $n - 1$, because one of the original faces has been replaced by n new faces. Hence $F - E + V$ is unaltered by this process. It is also unaltered if we add new edges without adding new vertices, for each new edge introduces one new face. Consequently $F - E + V$ is the same for any division obtained from a given one by adding new vertices, edges and faces, and therefore is the same for all divisions of the surface.

For the torus, the value of $F - E + V$ is zero. This can be seen at once from figure 5, in which there is one face, two edges and one vertex. Similarly, from figure 10 we deduce that $F - E + V = 1$ for the real projective plane.

Algebraic topology was originally based on the idea of dividing a topological space into elements corresponding to the vertices, edges and faces of polyhedra, and their generalisations to higher dimensions. By a study of such subdivisions of spaces, many topological invariants, among them the Euler characteristic (the expression corresponding to $F - E + V$) can be found. Some of these will be discussed in a later chapter.

7. The colouring of maps. Suppose that a country is divides into regions (for example counties or states) and a coloured map is to be constructed in such a way that no two regions with a common boundary have the same colour. A well-known unsolved problem is to prove that at most four colours are necessary to colour a map in this way. It can easily be shown that three colours are insufficient for certain maps; for example four colours are necessary for the regions A, B, C, and D of figure 12. It has been proved that five colours are always sufficient, but although it seems probable that this number could be reduced to four, no proof of this has yet been found, despite the fact that over a century has elapsed since the problem was first investigated. All that has been shown is that any map for which four colours are insufficient would necessarily be very complicated if it did exist.

There are map-colouring problems for other surfaces apart from the plane. The problem is effectively the same for any simply-connected surface, but the situation is quite different on a non-simply connected surface such as

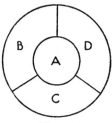

Fig. 12

the torus. Many of the map-colouring problems have been solved, despite the fact that the simplest case is still unsolved. For example, it has been shown that seven colours are sufficient for a map on the torus, and that some maps on the torus do require seven colours; for instance the map of figure 13, which covers the whole surface, requires seven

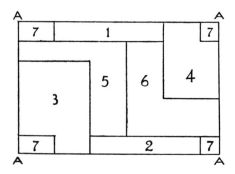

Fig. 13

colours since each region is contiguous with every other region.

Map-colouring is a topological problem, because it is concerned with relationships between regions on a surface which do not change when a topological transformation is made. The minimum number of colours required to colour a map on a given surface is called the **chromatic number** of the surface. It is another example of a topological invariant.

CHAPTER II

TOPOLOGICAL SPACES

In this chapter the idea of a topological space is introduced in its most general form. Many mathematicians regard topology as a branch of set theory, because topological ideas can be introduced into sets of any kind. This is the view adopted in the present chapter. At times the intuitive ideas of Chapter I may seem remote. A careful study of the way in which the axioms and definitions are formed is necessary for a full appreciation of their significance.

We begin with some notations and definitions of set theory †. From some considerations of continuity of functions of real variables, we arrive at the idea of a metric space. In such a space, continuity depends on 'distance', but it can also be expressed in terms of other concepts, which lend themselves to further generalisation to spaces in which distance is not defined, though continuity can still be discussed. Such spaces are called topological spaces.

8. Notations and definitions of set theory. A set is a collection of objects determined by some property. The members of a set are called its elements, and if a is

† The reader will find an account of sets of points in Euclidean spaces in W. W. Rogosinski's book *Volume and Integral*, Chapter I. Our notation and terminology sometimes differ slightly from Rogosinski's because of different traditions in analysis and topology, but it is not difficult to make the necessary modifications. In the present book we consider general sets, not necessarily sets of points in Euclidean space.

an element of a set A, we write $a \in A$. If x is a variable ranging over all elements of A, we write $A = \{x\}$.

If A and B are two sets such that every element of B is an element of A, then we say that B is a **subset** of A, and we write $B \subset A$ or $A \supset B$. In figure 14, the set A is represented by the interior of the larger circle, and B by the interior of the smaller circle.

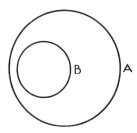

Fig. 14

The **union** $A \cup B$ of two sets A and B is the set of all elements which are in either A or B; this includes the possibility of being in both. The **intersection †** $A \cap B$ is the set of all elements which are in both A and B. In figure 15, the region shaded vertically represents $A \cup B$ and that shaded horizontally represents $A \cap B$.

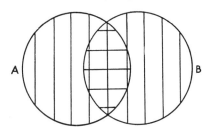

Fig. 15

† In Rogosinski's book, the union of two sets is called their *sum* and the intersection their *product*.

B

The **null set** O is the set containing no elements. If A and B have no elements in common, then $A \cap B = O$; in this case A and B are said to be **disjoint.**

If $B \subset A$, the **complement** $_cB$ of B in A is the set of elements of A which are not in B. It is also denoted by $A - B$. In figure 14, $_cB$ is represented by the portion of the interior of the outer circle which is outside or on the inner circle.

Let B_1 and B_2 be two subsets of A. Then

$$_c(B_1 \cup B_2) = {_cB_1} \cap {_cB_2}.$$

For if x is in A but not in $B_1 \cup B_2$, then it is in neither B_1 nor B_2 and so it is in both $_cB_1$ and $_cB_2$. Hence every element of $_c(B_1 \cup B_2)$ is also an element of $_cB_1 \cap {_cB_2}$, and so $_c(B_1 \cup B_2) \subset {_cB_1} \cap {_cB_2}$. If y is an element of A which is in $_cB_1 \cap {_cB_2}$, then it is in neither B_1 nor B_2 and so it is in $_c(B_1 \cup B_2)$. Therefore $_cB_1 \cap {_cB_2} \subset {_c}(B_1 \cup B_2)$; combining this with the previous result we see that the two sets $_c(B_1 \cup B_2)$ and $_cB_1 \cap {_cB_2}$ are identical. In a similar manner it can be proved that

$$_c(B_1 \cap B_2) = {_cB_1} \cup {_cB_2}.$$

The **direct product** $A \times B$ of two sets is the set of ordered pairs (a, b) where $a \in A$ and $b \in B$. Since the pairs are ordered, $A \times B$ is not identical with $B \times A$, unless $A = B$. Ordered pairs are familiar in elementary analytical geometry. If A is the set of real numbers, a point of the Euclidean plane can be represented in Cartesian coordinates by elements of $A \times A$. Similarly, if B is the set of positive real numbers, and C is the set of real numbers θ such that $0 \leq \theta < 2\pi$, then the points of the Euclidean plane, with the exception of the origin, are represented in polar coordinates by elements of $B \times C$. The concept of direct product can easily be extended to any finite number of sets; $A_1 \times A_2 \times \ldots \times A_n$ is the set of ordered 'n-ples' $(a_1, a_2, \ldots, a_n)$ where $a_i \in A_i$, $(i = 1, 2, \ldots, n)$.

9. Functions. The concept of **function** or **transformation** is of fundamental importance in topology. A function is always defined in terms of two sets, possibly coincident. For example, in elementary analysis we encounter functions of a real variable; these are defined over one set of real numbers and have values in another set of real numbers.

Any correspondence which associates with each element of a set A a unique element of a set B is called a function or transformation from A to B, and is denoted by $f : A \to B$. This is abbreviated to f when no confusion can arise as to which two sets are involved.

A function defined in this way is more precisely described as a single-valued function or a many-one transformation. The concept of function can be generalised to include cases in which more than one element of B may correspond to a given element of A; such functions are called multi-valued. In what follows the words 'function' and 'transformation' will be interpreted as 'single-valued function' and 'many-one transformation' respectively; however we sometimes retain the term 'many-one transformation' for emphasis.

If $a \epsilon A$, the element of B corresponding to a is called the **image** of a by or under f, and is denoted by $f(a)$. If $C \subset A$, the elements of B related to elements of C by f form a set $f(C)$ called the image of C by f.

If $b \epsilon f(A)$, the set of all elements $a \epsilon A$ such that $b = f(a)$ is called the **inverse image** of b by f. The correspondence which relates each member of $f(A)$ to its inverse image by f is called the **inverse** of f and is denoted by $f^{-1} : f(A) \to A$. In general, it is a multi-valued function. The inverse image of an element b of $f(A)$ is written $f^{-1}(b)$ and the inverse image of a subset $C \subset f(A)$ is written $f^{-1}(C)$. If b is not in $f(A)$, then its inverse image by f is defined to be the null set.

Let $f : A \to B$ and $g : B \to C$ be two transformations from A to B and from B to C respectively. Then their **product** is defined to be the transformation $h : A \to C$ where $h(x) = g(f(x))$. It is denoted by $g . f$.

If $f : A \to B$ is such that $f(A) = B$, then f is said to be a transformation of A **onto** B; a transformation $f : A \to B$ which does not necessarily satisfy this condition is said to be a transformation of A **into** B. Here we use the word 'into' in the wide sense; a transformation onto B is a special case of a transformation into B.

If $f(A)$ is a single element of B, then f is called a **constant transformation,** because it has the same value for all elements of A.

If f is a many-one transformation such that $f(a_1)=f(a_2)$ implies that $a_1 = a_2$, so that each element of $f(A)$ corresponds to a unique element of A, then f is said to be **one-one** or **biuniform.** If $A \subset B$, the transformation $i : A \to B$ defined by $i(a) = a$ is a one-one transformation called an **inclusion;** in particular, if $A = B$, the inclusion $i : A \to A$ is called the **identity.** If f is a one-one transformation of A into B, then f^{-1} is a one-one transformation of $f(A)$ onto A.

Example 1. Let A be the set of real numbers, and B the set of real numbers x such that $-1 \leqq x \leqq 1$. The transformation $f : A \to B$ defined by $f(a) = \sin a$ is a many-one transformation of A onto B. It can also be regarded as a many-one transformation of A into itself, since B is a subset of A.

Example 2. Let A be the set of real numbers and B the set of positive real numbers. The transformation $f : A \to B$ defined by $f(a) = e^a$ is a one-one transformation of A onto B.

It is important not to confuse a function f with the image of A by f. The symbols f and $f(A)$ mean two different things. However it is customary to write $f(x)$ to denote a function when we wish to stress that it is defined over a certain set whose typical element is x. We must be careful to distinguish between the cases in which $f(x)$ represents a function and those in which it represents an image.

10. Equivalence relations. Equivalences of various kinds were mentioned in Chapter I. We now give a mathematical formulation of an equivalence. Let A be any set, and let a relation R be defined between pairs of elements of A so that for each pair a, b in A it is known whether or not a is related to b by R. If a is related to b, we write aRb. Then, if the following conditions are satisfied, the relation **R** is called an **equivalence relation.**

(**E.**1) aRa (reflexive condition)
(**E.**2) aRb implies bRa (symmetric condition)
(**E.**3) aRb and bRc imply aRc (transitive condition).

The first property expresses the equivalence of an element to itself, the second expresses the fact that the order of matching of the elements is immaterial, and the third that the property of being equivalent carries over in a natural way from element to element.

There are many examples of equivalence relations in all branches of mathematics. Congruence and similarity in Euclidean geometry and homography in projective geometry are all equivalence relations. In the theory of numbers, congruence of integers modulo a fixed integer k is an equivalence relation. (An integer m is said to be congruent modulo k to an integer n if $m - n$ is divisible by k). In the theory of groups, the relation of conjugacy † is an equivalence relation.

The most significant feature of an equivalence relation is that it divides a set into mutually exclusive classes, each of which consists of all elements connected by the relation to any particular element of the class. These classes are called **equivalence classes.**

11.   Continuity on the Euclidean line. In the theory of functions of a real variable, a function f depending on a variable x (f is a transformation of one set of real numbers into another) is said to be **continuous** for $x = x_0$ if, given any real number $\varepsilon > 0$, there exists a real number $\delta > 0$ such that $|f(x) - f(x_0)| < \varepsilon$ for all values of x

† See, for example, W. Ledermann, *Introduction to the Theory of Finite Groups,* Chapter IV.

satisfying $| x - x_0 | < \delta$. If f is continuous for all values of x for which it is defined, it is called a **continuous function**. This definition is analytical, but the situation can be pictured geometrically. The set of all real numbers is represented by the Euclidean line, some fixed point O of which is chosen as origin; corresponding to the number x there is the point P on the line whose distance from O is equal to x, due regard being paid to sign. As usual, x is called the coordinate of P. Then f is a many-one transformation of the line or a subset of the line into the line itself. The most convenient picture is obtained by drawing a graph. This is done by using rectangular Cartesian coordinates (x, y) in the Euclidean plane; the graph of f is the set of points whose coordinates are of the form $(x, f(x))$. Intuitively, continuity is suggested by a graph without breaks, and an examination of the rigorous definition given at the beginning of this section shows that it is derived from this intuitive idea.

A convenient way of describing continuity is to introduce the idea of neighbourhood. Let P_0 be a fixed point of the Euclidean line, and let x_0 be the corresponding coordinate referred to some fixed origin. The set of points whose coordinates x satisfy $| x - x_0 | < \varepsilon$ is called the ε-**neighbourhood** of x_0; it consists of all points whose distance from x_0 is less than ε. For example, the set of points satisfying $1 < x < 3$ is the 1-neighbourhood of the point corresponding to $x = 2$. In terms of neighbourhoods, the definition of continuity can be restated as follows:- a many-one transformation f of the Euclidean line, or a subset of it, into the line itself is continuous for $x = x_0$ if, given any ε-neighbourhood N_ε of $f(x)$ there is a δ-neighbourhood N_δ of x_0 such that $f(x)$ is in N_ε whenever x is in N_δ.

Closely connected with the idea of neighbourhood is the idea of **open set**; later we shall express continuity entirely in terms of open sets. A set of points on the Euclidean line is said to be **open** if each point P of the set has, for some

ε, an ε-neighbourhood entirely in the given set. An ε-neighbourhood itself is an open set, for if x satisfies $| x - x_0 | < \varepsilon$ then $x = x_0 \pm \eta$ for some positive number η less than ε, and the $(\varepsilon - \eta)$-neighbourhood of x lies entirely in the original ε-neighbourhood of x_0. An open set is not necessarily an ε-neighbourhood; for example the set of points whose coordinates satisfy one or other of the conditions $0 < x < 1$ and $2 < x < 3$ is open but it is not an ε-neighbourhood for any value of ε. An example of a set which is not open is the set defined by $0 \leq x < 1$; no ε-neighbourhood of $x = 0$ lies entirely in the set, for every ε-neighbourhood of $x = 0$ contains a point whose coordinate is negative.

12. Continuity in the Euclidean plane. A real-valued function f of two real variables x and y is said to be continuous for $x = x_0$ and $y = y_0$ if, given any $\varepsilon > 0$, there exists a number $\delta > 0$ such that $| f(x, y) - f(x_0, y_0) | < \varepsilon$ whenever $[(x - x_0)^2 + (y - y_0)^2]^{\frac{1}{2}} < \delta$; if f is continuous for all values of x and y for which it is defined, it is called a continuous function.

The geometrical picture in this case is obtained by taking the variables x and y as rectangular Cartesian coordinates in the plane; the expression $[(x-x_0)^2 + (y-y_0)^2]^{\frac{1}{2}}$ is the distance between the points (x, y) and (x_0, y_0), and it corresponds to the expression $| x - x_0 |$ in the case of the Euclidean line. The function f can now be regarded as a transformation of the Euclidean plane into the Euclidean line. The graph of the function is a surface in three-dimensional Euclidean space.

By defining the ε-neighbourhood of the point P of coordinates (x_0, y_0) in the Euclidean plane to be the set of points whose distance from P is less than ε, that is the circle of centre P and radius ε, the definition of continuity can be restated in terms of neighbourhoods. An open set in the plane is defined in the same way as for the line. For example, the interior of any figure bounded by a polygon is an open set in the plane.

The above definitions of continuity depend on the idea of distance when interpreted geometrically. If P_1 and P_2 are two points, on the line or in the plane, the distance between them defines a real function d, whose value corresponding to the pair (P_1, P_2) is denoted by $d(P_1, P_2)$. Thus d is a transformation of the direct product of the line or plane with itself into the set of real numbers. The image of (P_1, P_2) by d is the magnitude of the distance between P_1 and P_2. In the case of the Euclidean line, $d(P_1, P_2) = |x_1 - x_2|$ where x_1 and x_2 are the coordinates of P_1 and P_2 respectively, referred to some fixed origin. In the case of the Euclidean plane, $d(P_1, P_2) = [(x_1-x_2)^2+(y_1-y_2)^2]^{\frac{1}{2}}$, where (x_1, y_1) and (x_2, y_2) are the coordinates. In both cases the function d satisfies the following properties, all of which are easily verified:-

(i) $d(P_1, P_1) = 0,$
(ii) $d(P_1, P_2) \geqq 0,$
(iii) $d(P_1, P_2) = 0$ implies $P_1 = P_2,$
(iv) $d(P_1, P_2) = d(P_2, P_1),$
(v) $d(P_1, P_2) + d(P_2, P_3) \geqq d(P_1, P_3).$

In the case of the plane, the fifth property expresses the fact that the sum of the lengths of two sides of a triangle is not less than the length of the third side, equality holding when the three points are collinear and P_2 is between P_1 and P_3.

13. Euclidean space of n dimensions. Euclidean space of any finite number of dimensions can be defined by direct generalisation of two and three dimensional Euclidean spaces, using the representations of points by means of rectangular Cartesian coordinates. A point P of n dimensional Euclidean space E_n can be represented by an ordered set of n real numbers $(x_1, x_2, \ldots, x_n)$ called the coordinates of P. For convenience, we write $P = (x_i)$. The distance $d(P, Q)$ between the points $P = (x_i)$ and $Q = (y_i)$ is defined by

$$d(P,\ Q) = \left[\sum_1^n (x_i - y_i)^2 \right]^{\frac{1}{2}}.$$

This function satisfies the properties (i) to (v) of § 12. Only (v) is not immediately obvious. If $R = (z_i)$ and we write $u_i = x_i - y_i$, $v_i = y_i - z_i$, then

$$d(P,\ Q) + d(Q,\ R) = \sqrt{\Sigma u_i^2} + \sqrt{\Sigma v_i^2},$$
$$d(P,\ R) = \sqrt{\Sigma (u_i + v_i)^2}.$$

But

$$\Sigma (u_i + v_i)^2 = \Sigma u_i^2 + 2\Sigma u_i v_i + \Sigma v_i^2$$

and therefore

$$[d(P, R)]^2 - [d(P, Q) + d(Q, R)]^2 = 2\Sigma u_i v_i - 2\sqrt{\Sigma u_i^2 \Sigma v_i^2}.$$

Since

$$\Sigma (u_i + \lambda v_i)^2 = \Sigma u_i^2 + 2\lambda \Sigma u_i v_i + \lambda^2 \Sigma v_i^2$$

is non-negative for any real number λ, we have

$$(\Sigma u_i v_i)^2 \leqq \Sigma u^2 \Sigma v_i^2,$$

and so

$$d(P,\ R)^2 - [d(P,\ Q) + d(Q,\ R)]^2 \leqq 0.$$

Now $d(P, Q)$, $d(P, R)$ and $d(Q, R)$ are all zero if and only if $P = Q = R$, and otherwise their sum is positive. Hence

$$d(P,\ R) - d(P,\ Q) - d(Q,\ R) \leqq 0,$$

which is the required result.

If A and B are subsets of two Euclidean spaces E_m and E_n respectively, a many-one transformation $f : A \to B$ is said to be continuous at the point $P_0 \epsilon A$ if, given $\varepsilon > 0$, there exists a number $\delta > 0$ such that $d'(P', P_0') < \varepsilon$ whenever $d(P,\ P_0) < \delta$, where $P' = f(P)$, $P_0' = f(P_0)$ and d, d' are the distance functions of E_m and E_n respectively. This is a direct generalisation of the definitions in §§ 11 and 12. Based on this definition of continuity, we could now develop topological ideas for Euclidean spaces.

However, the only properties of the Euclidean spaces that we would require for a general discussion are satisfied in a wider class of spaces. The significance of the function d is not in its defining formula but in the properties (i) to (v) of § 12. We now discuss these more general spaces.

14. Metric spaces. Let A be any set, and let d be a many-one transformation of $A \times A$ into the field of real numbers, so that d is a real-valued function defined over the set of all ordered pairs of elements of A. Then d is called a **metric** in A if it satisfies the following conditions:

(**M.1**) $d(a, b) = 0$ *if and only if* $a = b$

(**M.2**) $d(a, b) + d(a, c) \geqq d(b, c)$,

where a, b and c are arbitrary elements of A. A set A together with a metric d is called a **metric space** M; to emphasise which set and which metric are involved, we write $M = [A, d]$. For any given metric d the value of $d(a, b)$ is called the **distance** between a and b. The same set can be given different metrics; each distinct metric determines a distinct metric space.

The axioms (**M.1**) and (**M.2**) are suggested by the properties (i) to (v) of § 12. (**M.1**) is a restatement of (i) and (iii). Put $c = a$ in (**M.2**); then we get $d(a, b) \geqq d(b, a)$ and similarly $d(b, a) \geqq d(a, b)$ by interchanging a and b. Hence (iv) is satisfied. Put $b = c$ in (**M.2**); then, using (**M.1**), we get $d(a, b) \geqq 0$ and so (ii) is satisfied. Finally (v) follows from (**M.2**) by using $d(a, c) = d(c, a)$, which has already been proved. Thus (**M.1**) and (**M.2**) imply properties (i) to (v) of § 12. It is easily shown that, conversely, properties (i) to (v) imply (**M.1**) and (**M.2**). Thus Euclidean space E_n, with d defined as in § 13, is a metric space.

Any set can be given a metric; for the function d_0 defined by $d_0(a, b) = 0$ if $a = b$ and $d_0(a, b) = 1$ if $a \neq b$ satisfies (**M.1**) and (**M.2**) but imposes no restriction on the set A. This metric, though its properties are rather peculiar, does have its uses. We shall use it occasionally in illustrations.

When referring to transformations between the under-lying sets of metric spaces, it is convenient to regard them as being transformations of the spaces rather than of the sets, for we are nearly always concerned with relationships connecting the transformations and the metrics. Thus, if $M_1 = [A_1, d_1]$ and $M_2 = [A_2, d_2]$ are two metric spaces, we frequently denote a transformation $f : A_1 \to A_2$ by $f : M_1 \to M_2$.

15. Continuity in metric spaces. The definition of continuity given in this section depends essentially on the idea of distance. Subsequently, we shall express continuity in more general terms.

A continuous transformation from one metric space to another is defined by a direct generalisation of the definition of continuous transformations of subsets of Euclidean spaces. Let M_1 and M_2 be two metric spaces whose metrics are d_1 and d_2 respectively. A transformation $f : M_1 \to M_2$ is said to be continuous at the point $x_0 \epsilon M_1$ if, given any real number $\varepsilon > 0$, there exists a real number $\delta > 0$ such that $d_2(f(x), f(x_0)) < \varepsilon$ for all values of x satisfying $d_1(x, x_0) < \delta$. A transformation which is continuous at each point of M_1 is called a **continuous transformation** or a **mapping**. (Some authors use the word 'mapping' to mean merely a many-one transformation. In this book 'mapping' will always mean many-one *continuous* transfor-mation. We sometimes write 'continuous mapping' to emphasise the continuity.)

Our interest in the mathematical definition of continuity is due to the significance of the intuitive idea of continuous deformation in topology. However, it is clear that continuity alone cannot provide a mathematical definition of topo-logical equivalence, because a continuous transformation need not be one-one, so that the necessary symmetry is not attained. Indeed, any metric space can be transformed continuously into any other, for a constant transformation is always continuous. Even if we restrict our attention to continuous one-one transformations, we still do not obtain the desired symmetry, as the following example shows.

Example. Let A be the set of real numbers, d the Euclidean line metric defined by $d(x, y) = |x - y|$ and d_0 the metric defined at the end of § 14, so that $d_0(x, y) = 0$ if $x = y$ and $d_0(x, y) = 1$ otherwise. Let M and M_0 be the corresponding metric spaces. We shall first show that any transformation $f : M_0 \to M$ is continuous. Let δ be a positive number not greater than 1. Then $d_0(x, y) < \delta$ implies that $d_0(x, y) = 0$, since the only possible values of the function d_0 are 0 and 1. Therefore $d_0(x, y) < \delta$ implies that $x = y$. Hence, given $\varepsilon > 0$, there is always a number $\delta > 0$ such that $d_0(x, y) < \delta$ implies that $d(f(x), f(y)) < \varepsilon$, for, by choosing $\delta \leqq 1$ we can always ensure that $d(f(x), f(y))$ is zero. Hence f is continuous; for example the transformation defined by $f(x) = x$ is continuous. Thus M_0 can be mapped continuously onto M by a one-one transformation. Now suppose that M can be transformed continuously onto M_0 by a one-one transformation g. Then $g(x) = g(y)$ implies that $x = y$. Since g is continuous, there exists a number $\delta > 0$ such that $d(x, y) < \delta$ implies that $d_0(g(x), g(y)) < 1$, by applying the continuity condition with $\varepsilon = 1$. Choose x and y so that $|x - y| = \frac{1}{2}\delta$. Then $x \neq y$, but $d(x, y) < \delta$ and therefore $d_0(g(x), g(y)) < 1$; hence $g(x) = g(y)$ and so $x = y$. This is a contradiction; therefore there is no continuous one-one transformation of M onto M_0. In particular the transformation $g : M \to M_0$ defined by $g(x) = x$ is not continuous.

In order to define transformations which conform to the required conditions for an equivalence relation we insist on the continuity of both the transformation and its inverse. A one-one transformation $f : M_1 \to M_2$ of M_1 onto M_2 is called a **homeomorphism** or a **topological mapping** if f and f^{-1} are both continuous. If such a mapping exists, then M_1 is said to be **homeomorphic** or **topologically equivalent** to M_2.

It is easily seen that topological equivalence is an equivalence relation in the sense of § 10. The reflexive condition follows immediately from the fact that the identity transformation of a metric space onto itself is continuous. If M_1 is homeomorphic to M_2 there is a topological mapping $f : M_1 \to M_2$. Therefore $f^{-1} : M_2 \to M_1$ is also a topological mapping and so M_2 is homeomorphic to M_1. Thus topological equivalence is symmetric. Finally the transitivity of the relation can be proved by showing that, if $f : M_1 \to M_2$ and $g : M_2 \to M_3$ are topological mappings, then the product $h = g \cdot f$ defined by $h(x) = g(f(x))$ is also a topological mapping. This follows from the theorem that a continuous function of a continuous function is itself continuous; the proof of this theorem is postponed until the definitions of topological spaces and continuous transformations of topological spaces have been given.

16. Open sets and related concepts in metric spaces. The ε-**neighbourhood** of a point x in a metric space M is the set of points y such that $d(x, y) < \varepsilon$. The definition of continuity for metric spaces given in § 15 can be restated in terms of neighbourhoods in exactly the same way as for the Euclidean line (see § 11).

A point x in a metric space M is called a **limit point** of a subset X of M if every ε-neighbourhood of x contains a point of X other than x itself. The set of limit points of X is called the **derived set** and is denoted by X'. For example the points $x = 0$ and $x = 1$ are limit points of the set $0 < x < 1$ on the Euclidean line; and in this case every point of X itself is also a limit point. However, as Example 3 below shows, the points of a set X need not be limit points of X. The derived set in this case is the set $0 \leq x \leq 1$. For the metric d_0 of § 14, there are no limit points for any set, since the ε-neighbourhood of any point consists of the point itself when $\varepsilon \leq 1$.

A point x in M is called a **point of closure** of a subset X of M if either $x \in X$ or x is a limit point of X. The set of points of closure of X is called the **closure** of X; it is denoted by $\overline{X}$. It follows at once from the definition that $\overline{X} = X \cup X'$.

Example 1. Let X be the set of points (x, y) in two-dimensional Euclidean space satisfying $x^2 + y^2 < 1$, so that X is the interior of the unit circle whose centre is the origin. Then the limit points of X are either points of X, or are on the unit circle $x^2 + y^2 = 1$. These are also the points of closure, so that $\overline{X} = X'$, each being the set $x^2 + y^2 \leqq 1$.

Example 2. Let X be the set of rational points on the Euclidean line: that is, the points whose coordinates are of the form p/q where p is an integer and q is a positive integer. Then every point on the Euclidean line is a limit point, because every neighbourhood contains infinitely many rational points. Again $\overline{X} = X'$, both sets in this case being the whole space. (A set in a metric space M is said to be *everywhere dense* in M if its closure is M itself. Thus the set of rational points is everywhere dense in the Euclidean line).

Example 3. Let X be the set of points on the Euclidean line whose coordinates are of the form $1/n$, where n is a non-zero integer. Every point not in X, except $x = 0$, has a neighbourhood containing no point of the form $1/n$, and therefore $x = 0$ is the only limit point of the set. Thus X' consists of the single point $x = 0$, and $\overline{X}$ consists of this point and the points of X.

A set X of points in a metric space M is said to be **closed** in M if $\overline{X} = X$: that is, if X contains all its limit points in M. For convenience, the null set is regarded as being closed. From the definition it follows at once that the whole space M is closed in itself.

A set X of points in a metric space M is said to be **open** in M if every point of X has an ε-neighbourhood consisting of points of X alone. This is a similar definition to that given previously for the Euclidean line. For convenience, the null set is regarded as being open. From the definition it follows at once that the whole space M is open in itself. Thus, since the null set and M are also closed, the terms open and closed are not mutually exclusive.

Example 4. The set $0 \leqq x \leqq 1$ on the Euclidean line, and the set $x^2 + y^2 \leqq 1$ in the Euclidean plane are closed. The corresponding sets with $<$ replacing $\leqq$ are open.

Example 5. The set $0 \leqq x < 1$ on the Euclidean line is neither open nor closed.

Example 6. Any ε-neighbourhood is open. This can be proved as in § 11, for the Euclidean line.

Example 7. Let d_0 be the metric defined by $d_0(x, y) = 0$ if $x = y$ and $d_0(x, y) = 1$ otherwise. Then every subset of a metric space M of the form $[A, d_0]$ is both open and closed. For, if X is any subset, then X has no limit points and so $\overline{X} = X$; hence X is closed. Also, every ε-neighbourhood of a point x consists of x alone if $\varepsilon \leq 1$, so that every point of X has a neighbourhood entirely in X, and therefore X is open. This example shows that certain of the familiar properties of Euclidean spaces are not satisfied in a general metric space. For a subset of Euclidean space cannot be both open and closed in the whole space unless it is the null set or the whole space †.

In the above definitions of limit point, point of closure, closed set and open set the metric space M plays an essential part. The concepts are not intrinsic to the sets they describe, but are relative to the space M. A set X may be a subset of more than one metric space; being open or closed in one does not imply being open or closed in another even if the same metric is used.

17. Theorems on metric spaces.

THEOREM 2.1 *The intersection of a finite number of sets open in a metric space M is itself open in M.*

Proof. Let $X_1, \ldots, X_n$ be n open sets in M, and let X be their intersection. If X is the null set, it is open by definition. Suppose that X is not null, and let $x \in X$. Then there is an ε_i-neighbourhood of x consisting only of points of X_i, since x is in X_i and X_i is open; this is true for $i = 1, \ldots, n$. Let η be the smallest value of ε_i for these n neighbourhoods. Then the η-neighbourhood of x is contained in each set $X_1, \ldots, X_n$ and therefore in their intersection X. It follows at once that X is open.

This result is not necessarily true for an infinite number of sets open in M, as the following example shows. Let X_m be the set $-1/m < x < 1/m$ on the Euclidean line. Then X_m is open. But the

† See W. W. Rogosinski, *Volume and Integral*, p. 17.

intersection of all such sets is the point $x = 0$, for $x = 0$ is clearly contained in all the sets and $x = k$ $(k \neq 0)$ is not contained in X_m if $m > 1/|k|$; and the set on the Euclidean line consisting of the point $x = 0$ is not open. Thus the intersection of the infinite number of sets X_m is not open.

THEOREM 2.2 *The union of any number of sets open in M is open in M.*

Proof. Let $\{X\}$ be a collection of open sets, and let x be any point in their union. Then x is contained in at least one member X of the collection of open sets. Since X is open, there is a neighbourhood of x entirely in X, and so entirely in the union of all the sets. Hence the latter is open.

We observe that, in contrast to Theorem 2.1, Theorem 2.2 holds for an infinite number of sets as well as for a finite number.

THEOREM 2.3 *The complement $M - X$ in M of a set X is closed in M if and only if X is open in M.*

Proof. Let $M - X$ be closed in M. Then $M - X$ contains all its limit points, and so no point of X is such that every neighbourhood of it contains a point of $M - X$. Hence every point of X has a neighbourhood which contains no points of $M - X$ and which is therefore contained entirely in X. Consequently X is open.

Conversely, suppose that X is open. By a reversal of the above argument, no limit points of $M - X$ are in X. Therefore $M - X$ is closed.

THEOREM 2.4 *A point $x \in M$ is a limit point of a set $X \subset M$ if and only if every open set containing x contains a point of X other than x.*

Proof. Let x be a limit point of X. Then every ε-neighbourhood of x contains a point of X other than x. Any open set containing x is such that x has a neighbourhood lying entirely in the open set, and it follows at once that every open set containing x contains a point of X other than x.

Conversely, suppose that this condition is satisfied. Then, since an ε-neighbourhood is an open set, it follows from the definition of limit point that x is a limit point of X.

THEOREM 2.5 *A many-one transformation* $f : M_1 \to M_2$ *is continuous if and only if for every set* X_2 *open in* M_2, *the set* $X_1 = f^{-1}(X_2) \subset M_1$ *is open in* M_1.

Proof. Suppose that $f : M_1 \to M_2$ is a mapping. Then, given any point x of M_1, and an ε-neighbourhood N_ε of $f(x)$ in M_2, there exists a δ-neighbourhood N_δ of x in M_1, such that, if $y \in N_\delta$, then $f(y) \in N_\varepsilon$. This is a rewording of the definition of continuity given in § 15. Now let X_2 be a set open in M_2, and consider its inverse image $X_1 = f^{-1}(X_2)$. Let x_1 be a point of X_1; then $f(x_1)$ is in X_2. Since X_2 is open, there is a neighbourhood N_ε of $f(x_1)$ entirely in X_2. Therefore, by the continuity condition, there is a neighbourhood N_δ of x_1 such that the image of any point of N_δ is in N_ε. But N_ε is contained in X_2, and so N_δ is contained in $f^{-1}(X_2)$. Therefore $f^{-1}(X_2)$ is open in M_1.

Conversely, suppose that $f : M_1 \to M_2$ is a many-one transformation such that, for every set X_2 open in M_2 the set $f^{-1}(X_2)$ is open in M_1. Let x be a point of M_1, and N_ε a neighbourhood of $f(x)$. Then N_ε is open in M_2, and therefore, by hypothesis, $f^{-1}(N_\varepsilon)$ is open in M_1. Consequently there exists a δ-neighbourhood N_δ of x lying entirely in $f^{-1}(N_\varepsilon)$; thus N_δ is such that the image of any point of it is in N_ε. Hence f is continuous.

It can also be proved that f is continuous if and only if the inverse image of every closed set is closed.

18. Topological spaces. Metric spaces depend upon the notion of 'distance', which is clearly of no great significance in the study of topological properties, since it is not a topological invariant. Thus, although the spaces we have discussed are of a very general type, the method of defining them is to a certain extent unsatisfactory because their structures are determined by a non-topological

C

concept. In order to define a topological space in the best possible way, it is necessary to express the definition in terms of some structure which we can ensure will be topologically invariant. Then we can express all our topological ideas in terms of this structure and need never refer to a non-topological concept such as distance.

It has been found that the concept of 'open set' can be used conveniently to describe a structure of this kind. In metric spaces, open sets are topological invariants, because if two spaces are homeomorphic the image of an open subset of one under a homeomorphism is an open subset of the other — this is an immediate consequence of Theorem 2.5.

The object of proving Theorems 2.3, 2.4 and 2.5 of § 17 was to express the concepts of 'closed set', 'limit point' and 'continuous transformation' entirely in terms of the concept of 'open set'. Each of the theorems states a necessary and sufficient condition, and can therefore be used to frame an alternative definition. In each case this alternative definition avoids direct mention of the idea of distance, and involves the idea of open set instead. These definitions are therefore available for use in a wider class of spaces, which we call topological spaces. To define the structure of these spaces, we use the principal properties of open sets in metric spaces. These are provided by Theorems 2.1 and 2.2.

Let A be any set, and $\{U\}$ a system of subsets of A such that the following conditions are satisfied:-

(**T.1**) *The null set and A itself are in $\{U\}$.*
(**T.2**) *The intersection of two members of $\{U\}$ is in $\{U\}$.*
(**T.3**) *The union of any number of members of $\{U\}$ is in $\{U\}$.*

Any such system $\{U\}$ of subsets is called a **topology** for A. The set A together with a topology $\{U\}$ is called a **topological space** T, which we also denote by $[A, \{U\}]$. The elements of A are called the **points** of T, and the members of the system $\{U\}$ are called the **open sets** of T. A subset of A will be referred to as a subset of T.

An immediate consequence of $(\mathbf{T.2})$ is that the intersection of any finite number of open sets is open. By Theorem 2.1, this is true for metric spaces, provided that the open sets are defined as in § 16. Likewise $(\mathbf{T.3})$ is true for metric spaces, because of Theorem 2.2. The remaining condition $(\mathbf{T.1})$ is also satisfied in metric spaces as a consequence of the definition of open sets in metric spaces. Thus a metric space, in which the topology is the system of open sets defined in § 16, is a topological space; indeed our axioms $(\mathbf{T.1})$, $(\mathbf{T.2})$ and $(\mathbf{T.3})$ were chosen so as to ensure that this is so. A topological space is said to be **metrisable** if a metric can be introduced into A such that the open sets determined by this metric coincide with the open sets which constitute the topology. We shall prove later that a topological space is not necessarily metrisable. If a topological space is metrisable, the metric is not unique, except in the trivial case of a space with only one point.

Example 1. A topology can be defined in any set A by taking the open sets to consist of the null set and the set A itself.

Example 2. A topology can be defined in any set A by taking the open sets to consist of the null set and all subsets of A, including A itself. This topology is in fact the same as that which arises from the metric d_0 of § 14, for, as we have seen, every subset of a metric space with metric d_0 is open. This topology is called the **discrete topology** for A.

Example 3. Let A be the set of real numbers x such that $0 \leq x < 1$. Let the open sets consist of the null set and the sets $0 \leq x < k$ where $0 < k \leq 1$. Then A itself is open, and so $(\mathbf{T.1})$ is satisfied. The intersection of the sets $0 \leq x < k_1$ and $0 \leq x < k_2$ is the set $0 \leq x < k_1$ if $k_1 \leq k_2$, and so $(\mathbf{T.2})$ is satisfied. Finally, by using an analytical argument, it can be shown that the union of any number of sets of this form is also of this form, and so $(\mathbf{T.3})$ is satisfied.

Example 4. Let A be any infinite set. Let the open sets consist of A itself, the null set, and any set whose complement is finite. Conditions $(\mathbf{T.1})$ and $(\mathbf{T.3})$ are satisfied trivially. To show that $(\mathbf{T.2})$ is satisfied, we use the fact that the complement of the intersection of two sets is the union of the complements of the sets (see § 8). If both the complements are finite, so is their union.

A set X in a topological space T is said to be **closed** in T if $T - X$ is open in T. Theorem 2.3 ensures that, when the topology of T is derived from a metric, this definition of closed set agrees with the definition of § 16. A point $x \in T$ is said to be a **limit point** of a subset $X \subset T$ if every open set containing x contains a point of X other than x itself. This definition is suggested by Theorem 2.4; again it agrees with the definition given in § 16 for metric spaces. A point $x \in T$ is called a **point of closure** of a subset $X \subset T$ if every open set containing x contains a point of X. The set $\overline{X}$ of points of closure is called the **closure** of X.

Let T_1 and T_2 be two topological spaces. A many-one transformation $f : T_1 \to T_2$ is said to be **continuous** if, for every set U open in T_2, the inverse image $f^{-1}(U)$ is open in T_1. Theorem 2.5 ensures that, when the topologies of T_1 and T_2 arise from metrics, this definition agrees with the one already given for metric spaces. A continuous transformation between topological spaces is also called a **mapping**.

A transformation f of T_1 onto T_2 is said to be a **homeomorphism** or a **topological mapping** if it is one-one, and if both f and f^{-1} are continuous. Just as for metric spaces, homeomorphism between topological spaces defines an equivalence relation, the transitive condition (**E.3**) depending on Theorem 2.6 proved below. The fundamental property of a homeomorphism is that it is a one-one transformation which preserves the topology, because the images and inverse images of open sets are themselves open.

19. Some theorems on topological spaces. The theorems of this section illustrate the type of argument used in general topology. Theorem 2.6 is required for proving the transitivity of topological equivalence. The other results are used in § 20 in discussing alternative approaches to the definition of a topological space.

THEOREM 2.6. *If f is a mapping of T_1 into T_2, and g is a mapping of T_2 into T_3, then the transformation $h = g \cdot f$ is a mapping of T_1 into T_3.*

Proof. Since f is continuous, the inverse image by f of a set open in T_2 is open in T_1; since g is continuous, the inverse image by g of a set open in T_3 is open in T_2. Let X be any set open in T_3. Then $h^{-1}(X)$ consists of those elements of T_1 which are transformed by f into $g^{-1}(X)$; therefore $h^{-1}(X) = f^{-1}\{g^{-1}(X)\}$. But $g^{-1}(X)$ is open in T_2 since X is open in T_3. Therefore $h^{-1}(X)$ is open in T_1, and so h is continuous.

THEOREM 2.7. *If X and Y are two subsets of a topological space, then $\overline{X \cup Y} = \overline{X} \cup \overline{Y}$: that is, the closure of the union of two sets is the union of their closures.*

Proof. If $z \, \varepsilon \, \overline{X \cup Y}$, every open set containing z contains a point of $X \cup Y$, that is a point of X or a point of Y. If every open set containing z contains a point of X, then $z \, \varepsilon \, \overline{X}$. If there is an open set V containing z but not containing a point of X, and U is any other open set containing z, then, by (**T.2**), $U \cap V$ is open, and also it contains z; therefore $U \cap V$ contains a point of $X \cup Y$. Since V does not contain a point of X, neither does $U \cap V$, and hence $U \cap V$ contains a point of Y. Thus every open set containing z contains a point of Y and so $z \, \varepsilon \, \overline{Y}$. Hence, if $z \, \varepsilon \, \overline{X \cup Y}$ then either $z \, \varepsilon \, \overline{X}$ or $z \, \varepsilon \, \overline{Y}$ or both. Therefore $\overline{X \cup Y} \subset \overline{X} \cup \overline{Y}$.

If $z \, \varepsilon \, \overline{X} \cup \overline{Y}$, then every open set containing z contains either a point of X or a point of Y, and so contains a point of $X \cup Y$. Hence $z \, \varepsilon \, \overline{X \cup Y}$, and therefore $\overline{X} \cup \overline{Y} \subset \overline{X \cup Y}$. Combining this with $\overline{X \cup Y} \subset \overline{X} \cup \overline{Y}$, we see that

$$\overline{X \cup Y} = \overline{X} \cup \overline{Y}.$$

THEOREM 2.8 *The closure of $\overline{X}$ is contained in $\overline{X}$.*

Proof. Let z be a point of closure of $\overline{X}$. Then every open set U containing z contains a point of $\overline{X}$. Let y be a point of $\overline{X}$ in U. Then every open set containing y contains a point of X. But U is an open set containing y, and therefore U contains a point of X. Hence every open set containing z contains a point of X, and so $z \in \overline{X}$.

THEOREM 2.9 *A set X is closed if and only if $X = \overline{X}$.*

Proof. Suppose that X is closed. Then $T - X$ is open. Let z be any point of $T - X$. Then there is an open set, namely $T - X$, which contains z but does not contain a point of X. Hence z is not a point of closure of X, and so $\overline{X}$ is contained in X. But X is always contained in $\overline{X}$; hence $X = \overline{X}$.

Conversely, suppose that $X = \overline{X}$. Let z be any point of $T - X$. Then z is not a point of closure of X, and so there is an open set U containing z but not meeting X. Let V be the union of all the sets U as z varies over $T - X$. Then V is a union of open sets, and so, by (**T.3**), it is open. Moreover V contains $T - X$, since every point of $T - X$ is contained in one of the sets U. Also no point of V is in X, since no set U meets X. Therefore $V = T - X$, and so $T - X$ is open; hence X is closed.

From Theorem 2.8 it follows that $\overline{\overline{X}} = \overline{X}$. For, by definition, the closure of a set always contains the set, so that $\overline{X} \subset \overline{\overline{X}}$. Therefore, using Theorem 2.9, the closure $\overline{X}$ of any set X is closed.

THEOREM 2.10 *A many-one transformation $f : T_1 \to T_2$ is continuous if and only if for every subset $X \subset T_1$, $f(\overline{X}) \subset \overline{f(X)}$.*

Proof. Suppose that $f : T_1 \to T_2$ is a continuous mapping. If U is any set open in T_2, then $f^{-1}(U)$ is open in T_1. Let X be any subset of T_1, and let y be a point of $\overline{X}$. Then every open set containing y contains a point of X. Let V be an open set in T_2 containing $f(y)$. Then $f^{-1}(V)$ is open in T_1, and contains y. Hence $f^{-1}(V)$ contains a point of X, and so V contains a point of $f(X)$. Therefore $f(y) \epsilon \overline{f(X)}$, and so $f(\overline{X}) \subset \overline{f(X)}$.

Conversely, suppose that $f : T_1 \to T_2$ is such that $f(\overline{X}) \subset \overline{f(X)}$ for every subset X of T_1. Let U be a set open in T_2; define $W = f^{-1}(U)$. Then $f(T_1 - W) = f(T_1) \cap {}_cU$, where ${}_cU$ is the complement of U in T_2. By hypothesis $f(\overline{T_1 - W}) \subset \overline{f(T_1 - W)}$, and so $f(\overline{T_1 - W}) \subset \overline{f(T_1) \cap {}_cU}$. Let y be a point of closure of $T_1 - W$. If y is in W, then $f(y)$ is in U. But, by what we have just proved, $f(y)$ is in $\overline{f(T_1) \cap {}_cU}$, and therefore every open set containing $f(y)$ contains a point of $f(T_1) \cap {}_cU$, which is a contradiction since U is an open set containing $f(y)$ and U cannot contain a point of ${}_cU$. Therefore $T_1 - W$ contains all its points of closure, and so, using Theorem 2.9, $T_1 - W$ is closed. Hence $W = f^{-1}(U)$ is open, and so f is continuous.

THEOREM 2.11   *A one-one transformation $f : T_1 \to T_2$ of T_1 onto T_2 is a homeomorphism if and only if $f(\overline{X}) = \overline{f(X)}$ for every subset X of T_1.*

Proof. Suppose that $f : T_1 \to T_2$ is a homeomorphism. Then it is continuous, and therefore, by Theorem 2.10, $f(\overline{X}) \subset \overline{f(X)}$ for every subset X of T_1. Also, f^{-1} is continuous, and so $f^{-1}(\overline{Y}) \subset \overline{f^{-1}(Y)}$ for any subset $Y \subset T_2$. Let Y be the image of X by f. Then $f^{-1}(Y) = X$, and the preceding condition can be written $f^{-1}\{\overline{f(X)}\} \subset \overline{X}$, or $\overline{f(X)} \subset f(\overline{X})$. It follows at once that $f(\overline{X}) = \overline{f(X)}$.

Conversely, suppose that f is an one-one transformation of T_1 onto T_2 such that $f(\overline{X}) = \overline{f(X)}$ for every $X \subset T_1$. Then f is continuous since $f(\overline{X}) \subset \overline{f(X)}$, and f^{-1} is continuous since $f^{-1}(\overline{Y}) \subset \overline{f^{-1}(Y)}$, where $Y = f(X)$. Hence f is a homeomorphism.

The following example shows that, although the operation of closure is preserved by homeomorphisms, it is not necessarily preserved by continuous transformations.

Example. Let A be the set of real numbers, and construct two topological spaces T_1 and T_2 by giving A respectively the usual topology corresponding to the metric $d(x,\ y) = |\ x - y\ |$ and the discrete topology (see § 18). Then the transformation $f : T_2 \to T_1$ defined by $f(x) = x$ is continuous. But any subset of T_2 is closed in T_2; therefore, for example, the set X defined by $0 < x < 1$ is closed in T_2. Its image by f is the same set, but this is not closed in T_1, and so $f(\overline{X}) \neq \overline{f(X)}$. This shows that, even for a one-one mapping, the image of the closure of a subset is not necessarily the closure of its image.

20. Alternative methods of defining a topological space.
Let A be any set, and with each subset X of A associate another subset $\overline{X}$, called the closure of X, such that the following conditions are satisfied:

(K.1) $X \subset \overline{X}$
(K.2) $\overline{0} = 0$
(K.3) $\overline{X \cup Y} = \overline{X} \cup \overline{Y}$
(K.4) $\overline{\overline{X}} \subset \overline{X}$

Then the set A together with this operation of closure will be called a **Kuratowski space** (the axioms **(K.1)** to **(K.4)** are due to Kuratowski).

Immediate consequences of **(K.1)** to **(K.4)** are $\overline{\overline{X}} = \overline{X}$ for all X and $\overline{A} = A$. The first two conditions **(K.1)** and **(K.2)** are satisfied trivially in any topological space, provided that closure is defined as in § 18. Conditions **(K.3)** and **(K.4)** are also satisfied in any topological space, because of Theorems 2.7 and 2.8. Hence a topological space, with closure defined in the usual way, is a Kuratowski space.

In a Kuratowski space, let a set be called closed if it coincides with its own closure (see Theorem 2.9); then let a set be called open if its complement is closed. The system of open sets defined in this way forms a topology. To prove this, we must verify conditions **(T.1)**, **(T.2)** and **(T.3)**. Condition **(T.1)** follows immediately from **(K.2)** and the fact that $\overline{A} = A$. To prove **(T.2)**, let V_1 and V_2 be open sets. Then, by definition, $_cV_1$ and $_cV_2$ are closed.

Therefore $_c\overline{V}_1 = _cV_1$ and $_c\overline{V}_2 = _cV_2$. But, from (K.3), $\overline{_cV_1 \cup _cV_2} = \overline{_cV_1 \cup _cV_2}$. Hence $_cV_1 \cup _cV_2 = _c\overline{V_1 \cup V_2}$ so that $_cV_1 \cup _cV_2$ is closed. But $_cV_1 \cup _cV_2 = _c(V_1 \cap V_2)$, and so $V_1 \cap V_2$ is open. Therefore (T.2) is satisfied. To prove (T.3), we first prove the complementary condition, namely that the intersection of any number of closed sets is closed. Let X be the intersection of a system of closed sets. Then, if C is any set of the system, $X \subset C$. Therefore $C = C \cup X$, and so, by (K.3), $\overline{C} = \overline{C \cup X} = \overline{C} \cup \overline{X}$, so that $\overline{X} \subset \overline{C}$. But C is closed, and so $C = \overline{C}$. Hence $\overline{X} \subset C$, that is $\overline{X}$ is contained in all the sets of the system. Therefore $\overline{X}$ is contained in their intersection X, and so, since $X \subset \overline{X}$ by (K.1), $\overline{X} = X$. Hence the intersection of any number of closed sets is closed. Taking complements, we see that the union of any number of open sets is open.

We now show that the closure of any set X with respect to this topology coincides with $\overline{X}$. Since $\overline{\overline{X}} = \overline{X}$, the set $\overline{X}$ is closed. Hence, if x is such that every open set containing x contains a point of X, then $x \, \epsilon \, \overline{X}$, for otherwise the complement of $\overline{X}$ is an open set containing x but not meeting X. Conversely, if $x \, \epsilon \, \overline{X}$ and U is any open set containing x, then the complement Y of U is a closed set; if U does not meet X, then $Y \supset X$ and so $Y = \overline{Y} = \overline{X \cup Y} = \overline{X} \cup \overline{Y}$ by (K.3), whence $Y \supset \overline{X}$, which contradicts $x \, \epsilon \, \overline{X}$. Thus (K.1) to (K.4) can be regarded as alternative axioms for the definition of topological spaces. Theorems 2.10 and 2.11 provide alternative definitions of 'continuous transformation' and 'homeomorphism' which can be used if (K.1) to (K.4) are preferred to (T.1) to (T.3).

There are other sets of axioms equivalent to (T.1), (T.2) and (T.3). For example, the axioms can be based on the idea of 'closed set'. They are then the same as (T.1), (T.2) and (T.3), except that the words 'intersection' and 'union' are interchanged.

21.   Bases.   The ε-neighbourhoods of metric spaces are a special kind of open set. They form what is called a basis for the space. A system of open sets in any topological space is called a **basis** if every open set is a union of sets of the system. In metric spaces, a natural choice for a basis is the system of ε-neighbourhoods, but not every topological space is metrisable, so that this choice is not always possible. A basis can be chosen for any topological space simply by taking all open sets as a basis.

The following theorem is sometimes useful in proving that a given function is continuous.

THEOREM 2.12 *If $\{N\}$ is a basis for a topological space T_2, then a transformation $f : T_1 \to T_2$ is continuous if and only if $f^{-1}(N)$ is open in T_1 for every member of $\{N\}$.*

Proof. If f is continuous, $f^{-1}(N)$ is open, by the definition of continuity, since every N is an open set.

Conversely, suppose that $f^{-1}(N)$ is open for every set N. Let U be any set open in T_2. Then U is a union of sets in $\{N\}$. Therefore $f^{-1}(U)$ is a union of sets of the form $f^{-1}(N)$, and since any union of open sets is open, it follows that $f^{-1}(U)$ is open. Therefore f is continuous.

22. Relative topology. Let X be a fixed subset of a topological space T. Then X can be given a topology as follows. Let U be any set open in T. Then $X \cap U$ is said to be open in X. The system of all sets of this form is a topology for X. This topology is said to be **induced** by the topology of T, and is also called the topology of X **relative** to the topology of T. The conditions (**T.1**) to (**T.3**) of § 18 must be verified. The first part of (**T.1**) is immediate, because $X \cap O = O$; also $X = X \cap T$, and since T is open in itself, it follows that X is open in itself. To prove (**T.2**), consider the sets $X \cap U_1$ and $X \cap U_2$, where U_1 and U_2 are open in T. Their intersection is $X \cap (U_1 \cap U_2)$, which is open in X since $U_1 \cap U_2$ is open in T. Finally any system of sets open in X consists of sets of the form $X \cap U$ where U is open in T, and their union is of the form $X \cap V$ where V is the union of the sets U. Since T is a topological space, V is open in T, and therefore $X \cap V$ is open in X. Hence (**T.3**) is satisfied.

By a **subspace** S of a topological space T, we mean a subset of T together with the topology induced by that of T. The topology of a surface in three-dimensional Euclidean space is usually taken to be the topology induced by the topology of the Euclidean space.

A set U open in a subspace S is not necessarily open in the whole space T. Similarly a set closed in S is not necessarily closed in T. However, if S is open in T, then all the open sets of S are open in T, for, if U is open in S, then it is of the form $S \cap V$ where V is open in T; and $S \cap V$ is open in T, since both S and V are open in T.

If T is a metric space, any subspace S can be given a metric simply by taking over the metric of T. This metric for S is said to be the metric induced by the metric of T. It can easily be shown that the topology defined by the induced metric is the induced topology.

THEOREM 2.13 *If $\{N\}$ is a basis for a topological space T, and S is a subspace of T, then $\{S \cap N\}$ is a basis for S.*

Proof. Since any set N is open, a set of the form $S \cap N$ is open in S. Hence all we need show is that every open set of S can be expressed as a union of sets of the form $S \cap N$. Every open set of S is of the form $S \cap U$, where U is open in T, and so, since U is a union of sets in $\{N\}$, $S \cap U$ is a union of sets of the form $S \cap N$ as required.

Example. A basis for the topology of the Euclidean plane consists of the interiors of all circles (the ε-neighbourhoods for all values of ε). Let C be the circle consisting of the set of points (x, y) for which $x^2 + y^2 = 1$. The interior of a circle in the plane either does not meet C or meets it in an arc, with the end-points excluded. Hence a basis for the topology of C consists of the collection of all such arcs. These arcs are not, of course, open in the whole plane.

23. Identification. Let A be any set, and **R** an equivalence relation in A. Denote the set of equivalence classes by A^*; each element of A^* consists of a class of equivalent elements of A. Define a transformation $f : A \to A^*$ by assigning to each element of A the corresponding equivalence class. Let $\{U\}$ be a topology for A, and let $T = [A, \{U\}]$ be the corresponding topological space. We define a topology in A^* by calling a subset U^* open in A^* if $f^{-1}(U^*)$ is open in A. The conditions (**T.1**) to (**T.3**) are easily verified. The topological space $T^* = [A^*, \{U^*\}]$ defined in this way is said to be obtained from T by **topological identification.** The word 'identification' is used because a set of equivalent points is regarded as a single point of T^*; that is, the points of T are identified.

An immediate consequence of the definition of the topology for A^* is that the transformation f is continuous. This transformation is sometimes called the **natural mapping** of A onto A^*.

Example. Let A be the set of ordered triples (x, y, z) of real numbers not all zero. Define an equivalence relation in A by saying that (x_1, y_1, z_1) is equivalent to (x_2, y_2, z_2) if there is a real non-zero number λ such that $x_2 = \lambda x_1$, $y_2 = \lambda y_1$ and $z_2 = \lambda z_1$. The set of equivalence classes defined by this equivalence relation is called the **real projective plane** P_2: this definition should be compared with the geometrical definition given in Chapter I, § 2. The usual topology for P_2 is defined as follows. Consider the elements of A which satisfy $x^2 + y^2 + z^2 = 1$. These can be regarded as points on the surface of a unit sphere in three-dimensional Euclidean space. Every point of P_2 is represented by exactly two such elements of A, for if (x_1, y_1, z_1) is any representative of a point, then $(\lambda x_1, \lambda y_1, \lambda z_1)$ satisfies the required condition if and only if $\lambda = \pm(x_1^2 + y_1^2 + z_1^2)^{-\frac{1}{2}}$. Thus the points of P_2 are in one-one correspondence with the pairs of diametrically opposite points on the unit sphere. Suppose that the sphere has the usual topology: that is, the topology induced by the surrounding three-dimensional Euclidean space. Then P_2 is given the topology obtained from that of the unit sphere by topological identification. The equivalence relation on the sphere in this case is that in which two points are equivalent if and only if they are diametrically opposite.

24. Topological products. Let $T_1 = [A, \{U\}]$ and $T_2 = [B, \{V\}]$ be two topological spaces. A subset W of the direct product $A \times B$ will be called open in $A \times B$ if every point of W belongs to a set of the form $U \times V$ contained entirely in W, where U and V are open in T_1 and T_2 respectively. Then, if the null set is also regarded as being open in $A \times B$, the system of open sets defined in this way forms a topology for $A \times B$. Condition (**T.1**) is satisfied trivially. To verify (**T.2**), let W_1 and W_2 be sets open in $A \times B$; then any point of $W_1 \cap W_2$ is in sets of the form $U_1 \times V_1 \subset W_1$ and $U_2 \times V_2 \subset W_2$. Hence it lies in a set of the form $(U_1 \cap U_2) \times (V_1 \cap V_2) \subset W_1 \cap W_2$, and since $U_1 \cap U_2$ and $V_1 \cap V_2$ are open, $W_1 \cap W_2$ is open. Finally (**T.3**) follows from the fact that any point of a union of sets W belongs to a set of the form $U \times V$, in at least one set W and therefore in the union of such sets. A basis for this topology consists of the sets of the form $U \times V$.

The set $A \times B$ together with the topology $\{W\}$ defined in this way is called the **topological product** $T_1 \times T_2$ of T_1 and T_2. The concept of topological product can easily be generalised to any finite number of topological spaces.

THEOREM 2.14 *The transformations* $p : T_1 \times T_2 \to T_1$ *and* $q : T_1 \times T_2 \to T_2$ *defined by* $p(x_1, x_2) = x_1$ *and* $q(x_1, x_2) = x_2$, *where* $x_1 \epsilon T_1$ *and* $x_2 \epsilon T_2$, *are continuous.*

Proof. Let U be a set open in T_1. Then $p^{-1}(U)$ is the set of ordered pairs (x_1, x_2) where $x_1 \epsilon U$ and $x_2 \epsilon T_2$. Hence $p^{-1}(U) = U \times T_2$. Since this is a product of sets open in T_1 and T_2 respectively, it is open in $T_1 \times T_2$. Therefore p is continuous. Similarly, q is continuous.

The mappings p and q of Theorem 2.14 are called **projections**.

If $f : A \to B$ is a many-one transformation of a set A into a set B, the **graph** of f is defined to be the set of points of $A \times B$ of the form $(x, f(x))$, where $x \epsilon A$. Suppose that topologies are introduced into A and B. Then the graph G of f can be regarded as a subspace of the topological product of the corresponding topological spaces.

THEOREM 2.15 *The graph G of a continuous transformation* $f : T_1 \to T_2$ *is homeomorphic with* T_1.

Proof. G consists of the subspace of elements of $T_1 \times T_2$ of the form $(x, f(x))$ where $x \in T_1$. Define a transformation $h : T_1 \to T_1 \times T_2$ by $h(x) = (x, f(x))$. Then, given any element x of T_1, $h(x)$ is uniquely defined. Given any element $(x, f(x))$ of G, $h^{-1}(x, f(x))$ is uniquely defined, for $(x, f(x)) = (y, f(y))$ implies $x = y$. Therefore h is a one-one transformation of T_1 onto G.

Let U be a set open in G. Then U is a union of sets of the form $(U_1 \times U_2) \cap G$, where U_1 is open in T_1 and U_2 is open in T_2. Therefore $h^{-1}(U)$ is the union of the sets $U_1 \cap f^{-1}(U_2)$; hence it is open, and so h is continuous.

Let V be a set open in T_1. Then $h(V)$ is open in G, because $p^{-1}(V)$ is open in $T_1 \times T_2$, and $h(V) = p^{-1}(V) \cap G$. Therefore h^{-1} is continuous. Hence h is a homeomorphism.

25. Topological groups. We have seen how topologies can be introduced in a natural way into subsets, sets obtained by identification and direct products. We now give an example of the way in which topologies can be introduced into sets which already have some sort of structure, in such a way as to be of significance in relation to that structure.

A **group operation** in a set A is an operation, which will be denoted by a dot, such that, if a, b, $c \in A$, then

(i) $a \cdot b$ is defined and is an element of A,

(ii) $a \cdot (b \cdot c) = (a \cdot b) \cdot c$

(iii)   there is an element e (the identity) of A such that $a \cdot e = a$ for all $a \in A$,

(iv)   for each $a \in A$ there is an element a^{-1} such that $a \cdot a^{-1} = e$. A set together with a group operation is called a **group** †.

† See, for example, W. Ledermann, *Introduction to the Theory of Finite Groups*, **Chapter I.**

Group operations by themselves are of no topological significance. A set can possess a group operation and a topology independently, and neither need have any significance in relation to the other. However the two types of structure may be linked together, as they are in the concept of a topological group. A set A together with a group operation and a topology is said to be a **topological group** if the transformations $f : A \times A \to A$ defined by $f(a, b) = a \cdot b$ and $g : A \to A$ defined by $g(a) = a^{-1}$, are continuous.

Example 1. Let A be the set of real numbers, and let the group operation be that of addition. Then $f(x, y) = x + y$ and $g(x) = -x$. If A is given the usual topology, then f and g are clearly continuous, so that A together with these two structures is a topological group.

Example 2. Let A consist of three elements a, b, c and let the products of pairs of elements be defined by the table.

	a	b	c
a	a	b	c
b	b	c	a
c	c	a	b

Then A is a group with respect to this operation. Define the open sets of A to be the sets O, a, b, a and b, and A itself. Then these open sets determine a topology for A. Since $g(a) = a$, $g(b) = c$ and $g(c) = b$, the inverse image by g of the open set b is the set c. But the set whose only element is c is not open, and so g is not continuous. Therefore A is *not* a topological group with respect to the given group structure and the given topology.

The continuity of the group operations is necessary in order to link up the group structure with the topology. Example 2 shows that this requirement is not necessarily satisfied when a group operation and a topology are chosen at random. In fact, the types of topologies encountered in topological groups are comparatively restricted (though any group can be given a topology, for example the discrete topology). For example, the associated topological space is **homogeneous**: that is, given any two elements a and $b \in T$, there is a homeomorphism $h : T \to T$ such that $h(a) = b$. For the transformation $f : T \times T \to T$ defined by $f(x, y) = x \cdot y$ is continuous, and hence $h : T \to T$ defined by $h(x) = f(x, a^{-1} \cdot b)$ is continuous. Moreover it is one-one, and h^{-1} is continuous; therefore it is a homeomorphism. Finally, $h(a) = a \cdot (a^{-1} \cdot b) = (a \cdot a^{-1}) \cdot b = b$ and so h satisfies the required conditions.

Exercises.

(1). If A, B, C are any three subsets of a set X, prove that

(i) $_c(A \cap B) = {}_cA \cup {}_cB$

(ii) $_c(A \cap {}_cB) = {}_cA \cup B$

(iii) $A \cap {}_c(A \cap {}_cB) = A \cap B$

(iv) $(A \cap C) \cup (B \cap C) = (A \cup B) \cap C$

(v) $A \cap (B \cap {}_cC) = (A \cap B) \cap {}_c(A \cap C)$.

(2). If f is a many-one transformation of A into B, and A_1, A_2 are subsets of A, prove that $f(A_1 \cup A_2) = f(A_1) \cup f(A_2)$, and $f(A_1 \cap A_2) \subset f(A_1) \cap f(A_2)$. In the second case show that equality holds for all A_1 and A_2 if and only if f is a one-one transformation.

(3). Show that, if d is a metric, then the function d_1 defined by $d_1(x, y) = d(x, y)/(1 + d(x, y))$ is also a metric, and that it determines the same topology as d (that is, a set is open with respect to d_1 if and only if it is open with respect to d.)

(4). Let A be the set of real numbers, and let a subset of A be called open if it is A or the null set or if it consists of points x such that $x > k$ for some k. Prove that the open sets defined in this way form a topology for A.

(5). Prove that a transformation $f : T_1 \to T_2$ is continuous if and only if, for every subset C closed in T_2, $f^{-1}(C)$ is closed in T_1.

(6). If $M_1 = [A_1, d_1]$ and $M_2 = [A_2, d_2]$ are two metric spaces, show that the function d defined by

$$d\{(x_1, x_2), (y_1, y_2)\} = d_1(x_1, y_1) + d_2(x_2, y_2)$$

where $x_1, y_1 \in A_1$ and $x_2, y_2 \in A_2$ is a metric in $A_1 \times A_2$. Show that the topology of this space is the usual topology of the direct product defined in § 24.

(7). Prove that the closure of the intersection of two sets in a topological space is contained in the intersection of their closures, and give an example in which equality does not hold.

(8). If S, T are topological spaces homeomorphic respectively to S', T', prove that $S \times T$ is homeomorphic to $S' \times T'$.

(9). Show that, if a topological space has only a finite number of points each of which is closed, then it has the discrete topology.

CHAPTER III

PARTICULAR TYPES OF TOPOLOGICAL SPACES

26. Hausdorff spaces. For many purposes the definition of a topological space given in Chapter II is too general,
as some of the examples of § 18 seem to indicate. Consequently extra conditions are frequently imposed, amongst
them the **separation axioms,** the most common of which
is the Hausdorff axiom:

(**H**) *If x and y are any two points, there are two disjoint
open sets one containing x and the other containing y.*

A topological space satisfying (**H**) is known as a **Hausdorff space.** Of the spaces in the examples in Chapter II,
§ 18, only the second is a Hausdorff space. In Example 1,
the only non-null open set is the whole space, and so no
separation condition is possible. The spaces of Examples
3 and 4, however, do satisfy separation conditions which
are weaker than (**H**). In Example 3, the space satisfies

(α) *If x and y are any two points, there is an open set
containing one of them but not the other.*

In Example 4, the space satisfies

(β) *If x and y are any two points, there are two open
sets one containing x but not y and the other containing y
but not x.* Clearly (β) is stronger than (α). The space of
Example 3 does not satisfy (β), but any space satisfying
(β) satisfies (α). The separation conditions (α), (β) and (**H**)
are sometimes denoted by T_0, T_1 and T_2 respectively.

We have not yet proved that the space of Example 2 is
a Hausdorff space. This could easily be done, but a more
general result is the following.

THEOREM 3.1 *A metric space is a Hausdorff space.*
Proof. Let x and y be two points of a metric space. Then,

if $\varepsilon = \frac{1}{2}d(x, y)$, the ε-neighbourhoods of x and y are disjoint, for if z were a common point, we should have $d(x, z) < \frac{1}{2}d(x,y)$ and $d(y, z) < \frac{1}{2}d(x, y)$ which together would contradict (**M.2**). Since ε-neighbourhoods are open sets, it follows at once that a metric space is a Hausdorff space.

A corollary to Theorem 3.1 is that a topological space is not necessarily metrisable, for, as we have shown, there are topological spaces which are not Hausdorff spaces. From Theorem 3.1, it follows that a necessary condition for a topological space to be metrisable is that it is a Hausdorff space; but this condition is not sufficient. We shall not, however, pursue this matter any further as it is too complicated to be discussed here.

Returning to the separation axioms, the following theorem explains the significance of the axiom (β).

THEOREM 3.2 *A topological space satisfies* (β) *if and only if every subset consisting of a single point is closed.*

Proof. Let x be a point of a topological space T which satisfies (β), and let y be a point of $T - x$. By (β) there is an open set containing y but not x; the union of all such sets as y varies is open and contains $T - x$, but does not contain x since no individual member contains x. Hence this union coincides with $T - x$, which is therefore open; hence x is closed.

Conversely, suppose that T is a topological space in which every subset consisting of a single point is closed. Let x and y be any two points. Then $T - x$ and $T - y$ are two open sets; $T - x$ contains y but not x and $T - y$ contains x but not y. Therefore condition (β) is satisfied.

Since (**H**) implies (β), a corollary to Theorem 3.2 is that in a Hausdorff space every subset consisting of a single point is closed.

The properties stated in the axioms (**H**), (α) and (β) are clearly topologically invariant, because they are expressed in terms of open sets. Thus if a space satisfies one of the conditions, any space homeomorphic to it also satisfies the same condition. A more general result is the following.

THEOREM 3.3 *If* $f : T_1 \to T_2$ *is a one-one mapping of a topological space* T_1 *onto a topological space* T_2 *satisfying* (H), (α) *or* (β), *then* T_1 *also satisfies* (H), (α) *or* (β).

Proof. We shall prove the theorem for the case in which T_2 is a Hausdorff space. Similar proofs can be given in the other cases. Let x and y be any two distinct points of T_1. Then $f(x)$ and $f(y)$ are distinct points of T_2, since f is one-one. Since T_2 is a Hausdorff space, there are disjoint open sets U, V in T_2 containing $f(x)$ and $f(y)$ respectively. The inverse images of these sets are the disjoint open sets $f^{-1}(U)$ and $f^{-1}(V)$ of T_1, and these contain x and y respectively. Hence T_1 is a Hausdorff space.

The next two theorems show how the Hausdorff property carries over to subsets and to topological products.

THEOREM 3.4 *If* S *is a subspace of a Hausdorff space* T, *then* S *is also a Hausdorff space.*

Proof. Let x and y be two distinct points in S. Then they are also points of T, and so, since T is a Hausdorff space, there are disjoint open sets U, V containing x and y respectively. Then the sets $U \cap S$ and $V \cap S$ are disjoint open sets in S, containing x and y respectively. Therefore S is a Hausdorff space.

THEOREM 3.5 *If* T_1 *and* T_2 *are Hausdorff spaces, their topological product is a Hausdorff space.*

Proof. Let (x_1, x_2) and (y_1, y_2) be two distinct points of $T_1 \times T_2$. If $x_1 \neq y_1$, there are disjoint open sets U_1, V_1 containing x_1 and y_1 respectively. Then $U_1 \times T_2$ and $V_1 \times T_2$ are disjoint open sets in $T_1 \times T_2$ containing (x_1, x_2) and (y_1, y_2). If $x_1 = y_1$, then $x_2 \neq y_2$, for otherwise the points (x_1, x_2) and (y_1, y_2) would not be distinct. In this case there exist open sets U_2, V_2 which are disjoint and which contain x_2 and y_2 respectively. The sets $T_1 \times U_2$

and $T_1 \times V_2$ are disjoint open sets in $T_1 \times T_2$ containing (x_1, x_2) and (y_1, y_2) respectively. Hence the required open sets always exist, and so $T_1 \times T_2$ is a Hausdorff space.

27. Normal spaces. The following important separation axiom is closely related to (**H**), but is concerned with the separation of closed sets rather than points.

(**N**) *If X and Y are disjoint closed sets, there are disjoint open sets U, V such that $X \subset U$ and $Y \subset V$.*

A topological space satisfying (**N**) is called a **normal space**. A normal space is not necessarily a Hausdorff space, nor is a Hausdorff space necessarily a normal space. (See Exercises 1, 2 and 3 at the end of this chapter). However, if every point of the space is closed, then (**H**) is a consequence of (**N**). Thus a topological space satisfies (**H**) if it satisfies (β) and (**N**).

Corresponding to Theorem 3.1 we have the following result.

THEOREM 3.6 *A metric space is a normal space.*

Proof. If A is any set, and x is any point in a metric space, we define $d(x, A)$ to be the greatest lower bound of the distances $d(x, a)$ where $a \, \epsilon \, A$. Then if A is closed, $d(x, A) = 0$ if and only if $x \, \epsilon \, A$. For $d(x, A)$ is clearly zero if $x \, \epsilon \, A$, and if $d(x, A) = 0$ then, given $\varepsilon > 0$, $d(x, a) < \varepsilon$ for some $a \, \epsilon \, A$, and so x is a point of closure of A; therefore $x \, \epsilon \, A$ since A is closed.

Now let A and B be two disjoint closed sets in a metric space. Consider the set of points x such that $d(x, A) < d(x, B)$. If x is a particular point of this set, $d(x, A) = d(x, B) - \eta$ for some $\eta > 0$ depending on x. Consider the $\frac{1}{2}\eta$-neighbourhood of x. If y is any point of this neighbourhood, $d(x, y) < \frac{1}{2}\eta$. By (**M.2**),

$$d(y, a) \leqq d(x, y) + d(x, a).$$

Hence

$$d(y, A) \leqq d(x, y) + d(x, A)$$

and so

$$d(y, A) \leqq d(x, y) + d(x, B) - \eta.$$

But
$$d(x,\ B) \leqq d(x,\ y) + d(y,\ B),$$
and therefore
$$d(y,\ A) \leqq 2d(x,\ y) - \eta + d(y,\ B).$$
Since $d(x,\ y) < \frac{1}{2}\eta$, we get $d(y,\ A) < d(y,\ B)$. Thus the set of points x such that $d(x,\ A) < d(x,\ B)$ is open. It contains A because if $x \in A$ then (i) $d(x,\ A) = 0$, and (ii) $d(x,\ B) > 0$ because A and B are disjoint and B is closed. Similarly the set of points x such that $d(x,\ B) < d(x,\ A)$ is open and contains B. Clearly the two sets are disjoint, and so the theorem is proved.

THEOREM 3.7. *A topological space is normal if and only if, given any closed set A and an open set U containing A, then there is another open set V containing A such that $\overline{V} \subset U$.*

Proof. Suppose that T is a normal topological space. Let A be a closed set, and let U be an open set containing A. Since U is open, $T - U$ is closed. Also $T - U$ does not intersect A, since $A \subset U$. Therefore, by (N), there exist disjoint open sets V, V_1 containing A and $T - U$ respectively. Since $V \cap V_1 = 0$, and V_1 contains $T - U$, V is contained in U. Let x be a point of closure of V. Then every open set containing x contains a point of V. Therefore x cannot be in $T - U$, since if it were it would be contained in V_1, and V_1 does not intersect V. Hence $x \in U$, and so $\overline{V} \subset U$.

Conversely, suppose that T is a topological space satisfying the condition of the theorem. Let X and Y be any two disjoint closed subsets of T, and let U be an open set containing X but not intersecting Y, for example $T - Y$. Then, by hypothesis, there is an open set V containing X such that $\overline{V} \subset U$. Since $\overline{V}$ is closed, $T - \overline{V}$ is open. Since $X \subset V$, the set $T - \overline{V}$ does not intersect X. Further $T - \overline{V}$ contains Y, since U has no points in common with Y, and $\overline{V} \subset U$. Hence the disjoint open sets V,

$T - \overline{V}$ contain X and Y respectively, and therefore T is a normal space.

An important property of normal spaces is contained in the following theorem †, known as **Urysohn's Lemma,** which has applications in problems involving the construction of continuous mappings.

THEOREM 3.8 (URYSOHN'S LEMMA) *Let $\dot{C}$ be the space of real numbers u such that $0 \leqq u \leqq 1$ together with the usual topology. A topological space T is normal if and only if, corresponding to each pair of disjoint closed sets A, B, there is a continuous mapping $f : T \rightarrow C$ such that $f(A) = 0$ and $f(B) = 1$.*

Proof. If such a function exists, the space is normal. For consider the sets N_1, N_2 in C defined respectively by $0 \leqq u < 1/4$, and $3/4 < u \leqq 1$; these are open in C. Therefore, since f is continuous, $f^{-1}(N_1)$ and $f^{-1}(N_2)$ are open in T. But N_1 and N_2 have no common points and so $f^{-1}(N_1)$ and $f^{-1}(N_2)$ have no common points. Moreover $A \subset f^{-1}(N_1)$, since $f(A) = 0$, and $B \subset f^{-1}(N_2)$ since $f(B) = 1$. Hence T is normal.

The converse, namely that if a space is normal then such a function exists, is more difficult to prove. The proof will be divided into two sections; in the first f is constructed, and in the second it is shown that f is continuous.

(I) We first construct a system of open sets $U(t)$, in one-one correspondence with numbers of the form $t = p/2^m$, where p is a positive integer $\leqq 2^m$. These sets satisfy the conditions $\overline{U}(t_1) \subset U(t_2)$ if $t_1 < t_2$, and each set contains A but does not meet B. This construction is carried out in stages as follows.

Define $U(1)$ to be the complement of B. Since B is

---

† The proof of this theorem may be omitted at a first reading. The result is not used later in the book, but the reader is recommended to study the theorem and to examine other books on topology for applications. See, for example, Bourbaki's *Topologie Générale*, Chapter IX.

closed, $U(1)$ is open. Also $U(1)$ contains A, since $A \cap B = 0$. Therefore, by Theorem 3.7, there is an open set V containing A such that $\overline{V} \subset U(1)$. We write $U(\frac{1}{2})$ for V. This is the first stage of the construction.

At the second stage, we consider the pairs of closed sets $(A, {}_cU(\frac{1}{2}))$ and $(\overline{U}(\frac{1}{2}), B)$. Since $A \subset U(\frac{1}{2})$, and $\overline{U}(\frac{1}{2}) \subset U(1) = {}_cB$, both pairs consist of disjoint closed sets. Therefore, by Theorem 3.7, there are two further open sets, denoted by $U(\frac{1}{4})$ and $U(\frac{3}{4})$ respectively, such that

$$A \subset U(\tfrac{1}{4}),\ \overline{U}(\tfrac{1}{4}) \subset U(\tfrac{1}{2}),\ \overline{U}(\tfrac{1}{2}) \subset U(\tfrac{3}{4}),\ \overline{U}(\tfrac{3}{4}) \subset U(1).$$

At the third stage, we can define open sets $U(\frac{1}{8})$, $U(\frac{3}{8})$, $U(\frac{5}{8})$, $U(\frac{7}{8})$ by applying Theorem 3.7 to the pairs of sets $(A, U(\frac{1}{4}))$, $(\overline{U}(\frac{1}{4}), U(\frac{1}{2}))$, $(\overline{U}(\frac{1}{2}), U(\frac{3}{4}))$ and $(\overline{U}(\frac{3}{4}), U(1))$ respectively. Then

$$A \subset U(\tfrac{1}{8}),\ \overline{U}(\tfrac{1}{8}) \subset U(\tfrac{1}{4}),\ \overline{U}(\tfrac{1}{4}) \subset U(\tfrac{3}{8})\ \text{etc.}$$

Continuing in this way, we can define, at the nth stage, open sets $U(1/2^n)$, $U(3/2^n)$, $U(5/2^n)$ etc., by applying Theorem 3.7 to the pairs of sets $(A, U(1/2^{n-1}))$, $(\overline{U}(1/2^{n-1})$, $U(2/2^{n-1}))$ etc. Thus, for each number t of the form $p/2^m$, we can define an open set $U(t)$ containing A and such that $\overline{U}(t_1) \subset U(t_2)$ if $t_1 < t_2$. Moreover each set $U(t)$ is contained in $U(1)$, and so does not meet B.

We now define a transformation $f : T \to C$ by defining $f(x)$ to be the greatest lower bound of the numbers t such that x is an element of $U(t)$ and $f(x) = 1$ if x is in none of these sets. Then $f(x) = 0$ if $x \, \epsilon \, A$ and $f(x) = 1$ if $x \, \epsilon \, B$.

(II)   To prove that f is continuous, we prove

(i) *If $f(x) < b$, then $x \, \epsilon \, U(t)$ for some value of $t < b$. Conversely, if $x \, \epsilon \, U(t)$, where t is less than b, then $f(x) < b$.*

Suppose that $f(x) < b$. Between any two real numbers there is a number of the form $p/2^m$. Hence there is a number t_1 of this form such that $f(x) < t_1 < b$; then $x \, \epsilon \, U(t_1)$, since otherwise we should have $f(x) \geqq t_1$. Conversely, suppose that $x \, \epsilon \, U(t_2)$, where $t_2 < b$. Then $f(x) \leqq t_2 < b$.

(ii)   *If $f(x) > a$, then $x \in {}_o\overline{U}(t)$ for some value of $t > a$. Conversely, if $x \in {}_o\overline{U}(t)$, where t is greater than a, then $f(x) > a$.*

Suppose that $f(x) > a$. Let t_3 be a number of the form $p/2^m$, such that $f(x) > t_3 > a$. Then $x \in {}_oU(t_3)$. Let t_4 be a number of the form $p/2^m$, such that $t_3 > t_4 > a$. Then, since $\overline{U}(t_4) \subset U(t_3)$, it follows that $x \in {}_o\overline{U}(t_4)$. Conversely, suppose that $x \in {}_o\overline{U}(t_5)$, where $t_5 > a$. Then $x \in {}_oU(t_5)$ and so $f(x) \geqq t_5 > a$.

From (i) and (ii) it follows that the inverse image of the set $a < u < b$ in $C (a \geqq 0$ and $b \leqq 1)$ is the set $X \cap Y$, where X is the union of all the sets $U(t)$ such that $t < b$, and Y is the union of all the sets ${}_o\overline{U}(t)$ such that $t > a$. Since the union of any number of open sets is open, X and Y are open. Thus the inverse image of any ε-neighbourhood in C of the from $a < u < b$ is open. The only ε-neighbourhoods not of this form are of one of the forms $a < u \leqq 1$ or $0 \leqq u < b$. The inverse image of $a < u \leqq 1$ is open because if $f(x) \leqq 1$, then x is any point of T, and so the set of points x of T such that $a < f(x) \leqq 1$ is the union of the sets ${}_o\overline{U}(t)$ for $t > a$, which is open. Similarly the inverse image of $0 \leqq f(x) < b$ is open.

Thus the inverse image of every ε-neighbourhood in C is open. Therefore, since the ε-neighbourhoods form a basis for C, it follows, using Theorem 2.12, that f is continuous.

This completes the proof of Theorem 3.8.

28.   Convergence. A sequence of points x_n of a topological space T is said to **converge** to the point $x \in T$ if any open set U containing x contains all the points x_n for n sufficiently large. If x_n converges to x, we write $x_n \to x$ as $n \to \infty$. This definition is a direct generalisation of the definition of convergence for sequences of real numbers. In *general* topological spaces, many of the familiar rules relating to convergence are broken; for example, a sequence may converge to more than one point. However, if suitable restrictions are made on the topological spaces, most of the familiar properties can be retained. An example is given by the following theorem.

THEOREM 3.9 *In a Hausdorff space, a sequence x_n cannot converge to more than one distinct point.*

Proof. Suppose that, in a topological space T, $x_n \to x$ and $x_n \to y$ where x and y are two distinct points. Every open set containing x or y contains each x_n for n sufficiently large. Hence every open set containing x intersects every open set containing y. Therefore T cannot be a Hausdorff space.

In metric spaces, a necessary condition for the sequence x_n to converge is that, given $\varepsilon > 0$, there is an integer k such that, for p, $q > k$, $d(x_p, x_q) < \varepsilon$. For suppose that $x_n \to x$. Then, given $\varepsilon > 0$, there is an integer k such that $d(x_p, x) < \frac{1}{2}\varepsilon$ for $p > k$, since the $\frac{1}{2}\varepsilon$-neighbourhood of x contains all x_n for n sufficiently large. Hence $d(x_p, x_q) \leq d(x, x_p) + d(x_q, x) < \varepsilon$ for p, $q > k$.

Any sequence satisfying the above condition, namely that, given $\varepsilon > 0$ there is an integer k such that, for p, $q > k$, $d(x_p, x_q) < \varepsilon$, is called a **Cauchy sequence**. Thus we have shown that a convergent sequence is a Cauchy sequence. However a Cauchy sequence is not necessarily convergent. For example, in the metric space consisting of the real numbers x such that $0 < x < 1$ together with the usual metric $d(x, y) = |x - y|$, the sequence defined by $x_n = 1/(n + 1)$ is a Cauchy sequence, but it is not convergent since $x = 0$ is not a point of the space.

A metric space for which every Cauchy sequence is convergent is said to be **complete**. Thus the set of real numbers x such that $0 < x < 1$ together with the usual metric $d(x, y) = |x - y|$ is not complete. However, as is well-known in elementary analysis, the real Euclidean line is complete, for a necessary and sufficient condition for the sequence x_n to be convergent is that, given $\varepsilon > 0$, there is an integer k such that $|x_p - x_q| < \varepsilon$ for all $p, q > k$. It follows that completeness is not a topologically invariant property, for the Euclidean line is homeomorphic with the set of real numbers $0 < x < 1$ with the usual topology.

29. Compactness. Certain closed surfaces in three-dimensional Euclidean space, for example the sphere and the torus, are contained in a finite portion of the space, but others, such as the paraboloid, are not so contained. The term **compact** is suggested for surfaces in the former category. The topological notion of compactness is based on this. However an intrinsic definition is required; that is, one which does not depend on a surrounding space as the above intuitive idea does.

We first consider subsets which are both closed and bounded in Euclidean spaces. By a study of these subsets we obtain a characterisation of compactness in terms of open sets and so arrive at an intrinsic definition of compactness applicable to general topological spaces.

In any metric space M, a subspace X, having the induced metric and the induced topology, is said to be **bounded** if there is a number k such that $d(P, Q) \leqq k$ for all pairs of points P, Q in X. For example, the sphere $x^2 + y^2 + z^2 = 1$ in three-dimensional Euclidean space is bounded, because the distance between any two points on the surface is at most 2.

Boundedness has no significance in a general topological space, nor is it topologically invariant, so it is of no direct use in obtaining a general definition of compactness. However, by using Borel's covering theorem, boundedness of closed sets in Euclidean spaces can be related to certain systems of open sets, known as open coverings, and these provide a foundation for the required definition. A system $\{W\}$ of subsets of a topological space T is said to **cover** T if their union contains T, so that each point of T is contained in some set of the system; the system of sets is called a **covering** of T. In particular, if each set is open, the covering is called open, and if the covering consists of a finite number of sets, it is called a finite covering. The system of all open sets in a topological space is an open covering; more generally any basis is an open covering.

THEOREM 3.10 (BOREL) *If X is a closed bounded subspace of Euclidean n-space, then every open covering $\{U\}$ of X contains a finite open covering: that is, from the open sets $\{U\}$ which cover X, there can be selected a finite number which still cover X.*

No proof of this theorem is attempted here, since too many otherwise unnecessary details would be involved if one were given. Many textbooks on modern analysis contain the theorem in some form; see, for example, W. W. Rogosinski's *Volume and Integral*, § 1.16.

In virtue of Theorem 3.10, we define a topological space T to be **compact** if any open covering of T contains a finite open covering. Thus closed bounded subspaces of Euclidean spaces are compact.

To show that the intuitive idea of compactness agrees as far as possible with the general definition just given, it is necessary to prove the converse of Theorem 3.10, namely that if X is a compact subspace of a Euclidean space, then it is closed and bounded. This will follow from the next two theorems.

THEOREM 3.11 *A compact subspace of a Hausdorff space is closed.*

Proof. Let T be a Hausdorff space, and let X be a compact subspace of T. If $y \in T - X$ and $x \in X$ then, by (**H**), there exist disjoint open sets U and V containing x and y respectively. As x varies over X, the sets $U \cap X$ form an open covering of X. Since X is compact, a finite open covering can be selected. Let $U^* \cap X$ be a typical set of this finite open covering, and V^* the corresponding set containing y. Since all the sets V^* contain y, their intersection W is non-null. By (**T.2**), W is open. Also, W does not meet X, since otherwise it would intersect one of the sets $U^* \cap X$, which does not meet the corresponding set V^* and therefore does not meet W. Hence any point of $T - X$ is contained in an open set not meeting X. Therefore X contains all its limit points and so it is closed.

THEOREM 3.12 *A compact subspace X of a metric space M is bounded.*

Proof. Consider the open covering of X by sets of the form $N \cap X$, where N is a 1-neighbourhood of some point of M. Since X is compact, a finite open covering can be selected from this covering. Suppose that such a covering consists of the 1-neighbourhoods of the points $P_1, P_2, \ldots, P_m$. Let k be the greatest of the distances $d(P_i, P_j)$ $(i, j = 1, 2, \ldots, m)$. If P lies in the 1-neighbourhood of P_i and Q lies in the 1-neighbourhood of P_j, then $d(P, Q) \leqq d(P, P_i) + d(P_i, P_j) + d(P_j, Q) \leqq k + 2$, and so X is bounded.

Since a metric space is a Hausdorff space, Theorems 3.11 and 3.12 together imply that a compact subspace of a metric space is both closed and bounded. Thus, in particular, compact subspaces of Euclidean spaces are closed and bounded. Hence a subspace of a Euclidean space is compact if and only if it is closed and bounded. However, this result is not true in general metric spaces, for Borel's theorem is not necessarily true for spaces which are not Euclidean. For example, with the metric d_0 of Chapter II, § 14, the whole space is bounded since the distance between any two distinct points is equal to 1. It is also closed, but, if the underlying set is infinite, it is not compact. For an open covering consists of all the sets containing a single element and clearly a finite open covering cannot be selected from this.

The following three theorems give examples of the way in which compactness of one space implies compactness of others.

THEOREM 3.13 *A closed subspace of a compact space is compact.*

Proof. Let X be a closed subset of a compact space T, and let X have the topology induced by the topology of T. Suppose that $\{U\}$ is any open covering of X. Then each set U is of the form $V \cap X$, where V is open in T. The system of sets $\{V\}$, together with the set $T - X$, which is open because X is closed, form an open covering of T. Since T is compact, a finite open covering $\{V^*\}$ of T can be selected. Then the system $\{V^* \cap X\}$ is finite and covers X, and so X is compact.

From its definition, compactness is clearly a topologically invariant property. The next theorem proves a stronger result, namely that compactness is invariant under continuous transformations.

THEOREM 3.14 *If $f : T_1 \to T_2$ is a continuous mapping of a compact space T_1 into a topological space T_2, then $f(T_1)$ is compact.*

Proof. Let $\{U\}$ be an open covering of $f(T_1)$. Then each set $f^{-1}(U)$ is open in T_1, since f is continuous. The sets $\{f^{-1}(U)\}$ form an open covering of T_1, since otherwise there would be a point of $f(T_1)$ not in one of the sets U. But T_1 is compact and therefore this covering contains a finite open covering $\{f^{-1}(U^*)\}$. The sets $\{U^*\}$ form a finite open covering of $f(T_1)$, and so the latter is compact.

COROLLARY. *A space T^* obtained from a compact topological space T by topological identification is itself compact.*

Proof. The natural mapping $f : T \to T^*$, defined by associating with each element of T the corresponding equivalence class, is a continuous transformation of T onto T^*. Hence, by Theorem 3.14, T^* is compact if T is compact.

Example. The sphere is a closed bounded subset of three-dimensional Euclidean space, and therefore it is compact. The real projective plane is also compact because it can be obtained from the sphere by topological identification.

THEOREM 3.15 *The topological product $T_1 \times T_2$ is compact if and only if both T_1 and T_2 are compact.*

Proof. Suppose that $T_1 \times T_2$ is compact. Then, by Theorem 2.14, the transformation $p : T_1 \times T_2 \to T_1$ defined by $p(x, y) = x(x \in T_1, y \in T_2)$ is continuous. Therefore, by Theorem 3.14, $p(T_1 \times T_2) = T_1$ is compact. Similarly T_2 is compact.

Conversely, suppose that T_1 and T_2 are both compact. If $\{W_\alpha\}$ is an open covering of $T_1 \times T_2$, each set W_α is a union of sets of the form $U_\beta \times V_\beta$, where U_β, V_β are open in T_1, T_2 respectively. For each $y \in T_2$, let S_y be the system of sets U_β for which $y \in V_\beta$. Then S_y is an open covering of T_1. Since T_1 is compact, S_y contains a finite open covering $U_{\beta_1}, \ldots, U_{\beta_n}$ of T_1. Let V^* be the intersection of the corresponding sets $V_{\beta_1}, \ldots, V_{\beta_n}$. Then V^* is open in T_2, and $y \in V^*$. If S^* denotes the system of all sets V^* obtained in this way, for all $y \in T_2$, then S^* is an open covering of T_2. Since T_2 is compact, S^* contains a finite open covering $V_1^*, \ldots, V_m^*$ of T_2. For each of these sets, we consider the corresponding sets $U_{\beta_1} \times V_{\beta_1}, \ldots,$ $U_{\beta_n} \times V_{\beta_n}$ and, for each of these, the set W_α containing it. The finite collection of sets W_α so obtained covers $T_1 \times T_2$. Hence $T_1 \times T_2$ is compact.

An important property of compactness is proved in the final theorem of this section.

THEOREM 3.16 *If $f : T_1 \to T_2$ is a continuous one-one transformation of a compact space T_1 onto a Hausdorff space T_2, then f is a homeomorphism.*

Proof. Let C be any set closed in T_1. Then, by Theorem 3.13, it is compact. Hence by Theorem 3.14 its image by f is compact, and is therefore, by Theorem 3.11, closed in T_2. Thus f transforms closed sets of T_1 onto closed sets of T_2. If U is any set open in T_1, $f(U)$ is open, for $X = T_1 - U$ is closed and so $f(X)$ is closed, whence $f(U) = f(T_1 - X) = T_2 - f(X)$ is open. Hence f maps open sets of T_1 onto open sets of T_2 and so f^{-1} is continuous.

But f is continuous and is a one-one transformation of T_1 onto T_2 by hypothesis. Therefore it is a homeomorphism.

The compactness of T_1 plays an essential part in this theorem. In Chapter II, § 15, an example was given of a continuous one-one transformation which is not a homeomorphism. In this case the transformation operates on a non-compact space.

A space is said to be **locally compact** if every point lies in an open set whose closure is compact. Clearly a compact space is locally compact; Euclidean spaces are examples of spaces which are locally compact but not compact.

30.   Connectedness. If a topological space T is such that there exist two disjoint non-null sets X_1 and X_2, both open in T and such that $X_1 \cup X_2 = T$, then T is said to be **disconnected**. The sets X_1 and X_2 are said to form a **partition** of T. Since X_2 is the complement of the open set X_1, it is closed as well as open. Similarly X_1 is closed as well as open.

A topological space which does not admit a partition is said to be **connected**. A subset of T is said to be connected if it is connected with respect to the induced topology. Two points x and y in a topological space T are said to be **connected in T** if they are contained in a connected subset of T.

THEOREM 3.17 *A topological space is connected if and only if the only non-null subset which is both open and closed in T is T itself.*

Proof. Suppose that T is connected and that X is a non-null subset which is both open and closed. Then $_cX = 0$, for otherwise X and $_cX$ would form a partition of T. Hence $X = T$.

Conversely, if the only non-null subset which is both open and closed is T itself, then T cannot admit a partition and so it is connected.

THEOREM 3.18 *If A is a connected subset of a topological space T, and B is a subset such that $A \subset B \subset \bar{A}$, then B is connected. In particular, $\bar{A}$ is connected.*

Proof. Let X be a non-null subset of B, both open and closed in B. Since $B \subset \bar{A}$, X contains at least one point of A, because every point of B is a point of closure of A and X is an open set. Similarly, if $_cX$ is non-null, it intersects A. The set $X \cap A$ is both open and closed in A and is non-null. Since A is connected, it follows, using Theorem 3.17, that $X \cap A = A$. Therefore $A \subset X$, and so $_cX \cap A = 0$, whence $_cX = 0$. Therefore $X = B$, and so B is connected, by Theorem 3.17.

THEOREM 3.19 *If $\{A\}$ is a system of connected sets having a non-null intersection, the union of the sets A is connected.*

Proof. Let B be the union of all the sets of the system, and let X be a non-null open and closed subset of B. Since X is non-null, it intersects at least one set A_1 of the system. The set $X \cap A_1$ is a non-null open and closed subset of A_1; therefore, since A_1 is connected, $X \cap A_1 = A_1$. Hence $A_1 \subset X$. But A_1 intersects any other set of the system, and therefore X intersects every set of the system. Hence, by the argument just used, $A \subset X$ for each set A. Therefore $B \subset X$, and so $X = B$. It follows, using Theorem 3.17, that B is connected.

THEOREM 3.20 *If a system of connected sets is such that one member of the system intersects every other member, then their union is connected.*

Proof. If A_1 is the member of the system which intersects any member A, then, by Theorem 3.19, $A_1 \cup A$ is connected. The system of sets $\{A_1 \cup A\}$ has a non-null intersection, since each set contains A_1. Therefore, by Theorem 3.19, their union, which is the same as the union of the sets A, is connected.

The next two theorems can be compared with Theorems 3.14 and 3.15.

THEOREM 3.21. *If T_1 is a connected topological space and $f : T_1 \to T_2$ is a continuous mapping of T_1 into a topological space T_2, then $f(T_1)$ is connected.*

Proof. Let X be any non-null open and closed subset of $f(T_1)$. Then $f^{-1}(X)$ is a non-null open and closed subset of T_1. Therefore, since T_1 is connected, $f^{-1}(X) = T_1$. Hence $X = f(T_1)$, and so $f(T_1)$ is connected.

THEOREM 3.22 *The topological product $T_1 \times T_2$ is connected if and only if both T_1 and T_2 are connected.*

Proof. Let x and y be points of T_1 and T_2 respectively. The sets $T_1 \times y$ and $x \times T_2$ are homeomorphic with T_1 and T_2 respectively. Hence they are connected. Also they have a non-null intersection, namely the point (x, y), and so, by Theorem 3.19, their union $E_{x, y}$ is connected. But $T_1 \times T_2$ is the union of all sets of this form, and $E_{x, y}$ meets $E_{a, b}$ in (a, y). If (a, b) is a fixed point of $T_1 \times T_2$, then $E_{a, b}$ is a fixed subset. Hence, using Theorem 3.20, $T_1 \times T_2$ is connected.

Conversely, suppose that $T_1 \times T_2$ is connected. Since the projections $p : T_1 \times T_2 \to T_1$ and $q : T_1 \times T_2 \to T_2$ are continuous, it follows from Theorem 3.21 that T_1 and T_2 are both connected.

Example. To prove that the Euclidean space E_n is connected, we need only show that E_1 is connected, for $E_n = E_{n-1} \times E_1$. To prove that E_1 is connected, we first show that the subset $0 \leq x \leq k$ is connected. Suppose that it is not; then it is the union of two disjoint non-null open and closed sets X and Y. Let X be the set containing $x = 0$. Define h to be the least upper bound of the numbers $x \in X$ such that $x < y$ for all $y \in Y$. Then $h \in X$ since X is closed and h is the *least* upper bound. But every ε-neighbourhood of h contains a point of Y, because otherwise h would not be an upper bound of numbers x such that $x < y$ for all $y \in Y$. Hence $h \in \bar{Y}$, and so, since Y is closed, $h \in Y$. This is contrary to the supposition that X and Y are disjoint, and so the set $0 \leq x \leq k$ is connected. Similarly $- k \leq x \leq 0$ is connected, and therefore, since E_1 is the union of all sets of these forms, E_1 is connected.

THEOREM 3.23 *If every two points of a set A are connected in A, then A is a connected set.*

E

Proof. Suppose that X and Y are disjoint non-null sets open and closed in A, such that $X \cup Y = A$. If $x \in X$ and $y \in Y$, then there is, by hypothesis, a connected subset $B \subset A$ containing both x and y. Therefore $B \cap X$ and $B \cap Y$ are non-null. Since X and Y are disjoint, $B \cap X$ and $B \cap Y$ are disjoint; also $B \cap X$ and $B \cap Y$ are both open and closed in B, since X and Y are both open and closed in A. Therefore B is disconnected, which is a contradiction, and so A must be connected.

If x and y are any two points in a set A, the relation of being connected in A is an equivalence relation. The reflexivity and the symmetry of the relation are immediate. To prove transitivity, we use Theorem 3.19. Suppose that x and y are connected in A, and that y and z are connected in A. Then there is a connected set $X \subset A$ such that x and y are both in X and a connected set $Y \subset A$ such that y and z are both in Y. Since X and Y both contain y, their intersection is non-null, and hence, by Theorem 3.19, their union $X \cup Y$ is connected. But $X \cup Y$ contains both x and z, and therefore x and z are connected in A.

The equivalence classes determined by this equivalence relation are called the **components** of the set A. Thus a set A can be divided into a system of disjoint subsets C; each set C consists of points which are connected in A. From Theorem 3.23, it follows that each component of a set A is connected, for every pair of points of a given component C are connected in C.

THEOREM 3.24 *The components of a set A are closed in A.*

Proof. If $x \in C$ and $y \in \overline{C}$, then there exists a connected set containing x and y, namely $\overline{C}$ itself, which is connected by Theorem 3.18. Hence $\overline{C} \subset C$, and so C is closed.

A topological space T is said to be **locally connected** if, for every point $x \in T$ and every open set U containing

x, there exists an open set V containing x and a connected set S such that $V \subset S \subset U$.

THEOREM 3.25 *A topological space T is locally connected if and only if each component of an open set is open.*

Proof. Let C be a component of an open set $U \subset T$. If T is locally connected, and if $x \in C$, there exists an open set V containing x and a connected set S such that $V \subset S \subset U$. Therefore every point of V is contained in the component C. Therefore C is a union of open sets, and so it is open.

Conversely, suppose that each component of any open set in a topological space T is open. Given $x \in U \subset T$, the component of x contains x and is such that every point is contained in a connected set $S \subset U$. Therefore T is locally connected.

THEOREM 3.26 *If $f : T_1 \to T_2$ is a continuous mapping of a locally connected space T_1 onto a topological space T_2, such that $f(U)$ is open in T_2 for every set U open in T_1, then T_2 is locally connected.*

Proof. Since T_1 is locally connected, then, for every point $x \in T_1$ and open set U containing x, there is an open set V containing x and a connected set S such that $V \subset S \subset U$. Consider the point $f(x) \in T_2$. Let W be an open set containing $f(x)$. Since f is continuous, $f^{-1}(W)$ is an open set containing x. Therefore there is an open set V containing x and a connected set S such that $V \subset S \subset f^{-1}(W)$. Consider the sets $f(V)$ and $f(S)$. By hypothesis $f(V)$ is open, and, by Theorem 3.21, $f(S)$ is connected. Since $V \subset S \subset f^{-1}(W)$, $f(V) \subset f(S) \subset W$. Therefore T_2 is locally connected.

A topological space T is said to be **arc-wise connected** if any two points in it are contained in a set which is homeomorphic with the set of real numbers x satisfying $0 \leq x \leq 1$, together with the usual topology. The intuitive idea behind this is one of a space in which any two points can be joined by an arc, that is, a continuous curve. Most of the familiar topological spaces are arc-wise connected.

Exercises.

(1). Let A be a set consisting of three elements a, b and c. Show that a topology can be defined in A by taking the open sets to be A itself, the null set and the subsets consisting of (i) a alone and (ii) the two elements b and c. Prove that the resulting topological space is a normal space which is not a Hausdorff space.

(2). Let A be the set of real numbers x satisfying either $0 < x < \frac{1}{2}$ or $\frac{1}{2} < x < 1$. Show that the sets $\alpha < x < \beta$ $(0 \leqq \alpha \leqq \frac{1}{2}, \frac{1}{2} \leqq \beta \leqq 1, x \neq \frac{1}{2})$ form a topology for A, such that the resulting topological space is a normal space which is not a Hausdorff space.

(3). Let A be the set of real numbers x satisfying $0 \leqq x \leqq 1$, and let a subset $U \subset A$ be called open if for each point x of U there is an integer n such that all the rational numbers in A whose distance from x is less than $1/n$ are also in U. Prove that this defines a topology in A, and that the resulting space is a Hausdorff space which is not a normal space.

(4). Prove that the space of Example 4 of § 18 is compact.

(5). Prove that a compact Hausdorff space is a normal space.

(6). Show that, in the space of Example 3 of § 18 the sequence $x_n = 1/(n + 1)$ converges to every point of the space.

(7). Prove that the topological space defined in exercise 2 is not connected.

(8). Show that a topological space T is connected if and only if every continuous mapping $f : T \to D$ of T into a space D, consisting of more than one point, with the discrete topology is a constant transformation.

(9). Use the result of exercise 8 to prove Theorems 3.19, 3.21 and 3.22.

CHAPTER IV

HOMOTOPY

31. Introduction. The concept of **homotopy** was mentioned briefly in Chapter I, § 4. We now discuss it in greater detail. Roughly speaking, two subspaces† of a topological space T are homotopic if one can be transformed into the other by a continuous deformation. Consider, for example, the case of simple arcs in T; by a simple arc we mean the image by a continuous mapping $f : C_1 \to T$, where C_1 is the space of real numbers u such that $a \leq u \leq b$, together with the usual topology, that is, the topology determined by the metric $d(u, v) = |u - v|$. If α and β are two simple arcs, then α is said to be homotopic to β if it can be transformed continuously into β. As indicated in figure 16, this means that there is a set of intermediate

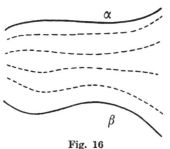

Fig. 16

arcs, some of which are denoted by the dotted lines in the figure, which correspond to the various stages of the deformation. Since the deformation is continuous, we require

† Strictly speaking, a homotopy is a relation between mappings and not between subspaces. A strict definition is given at the end of this section.

this family of arcs to vary continuously. In order to formulate the idea mathematically, we assume that the intermediate arcs are in one-one correspondence with the set of real numbers between 0 and 1. Thus we define a family of arcs α_v $(0 \leq v \leq 1)$ such that $\alpha_0 = \alpha$, $\alpha_1 = \beta$ and such that α_v varies continuously with v. This continuity must be expressed in mathematical form by means of some continuous mapping F into T, which depends on v as well as on the points of C_1; the image by F corresponding to a given value of v should be α_v. Suppose we take F to be a transformation of $C_1 \times C$ into T, where C is the space of real numbers v such that $0 \leq v \leq 1$ together with the usual topology. Then, if F is continuous, and if $F(u, v)$ for each value of v defines the arc α_v — in particular $F(u, 0)$ defines α and $F(u, 1)$ defines β — then the function F does determine a continuous deformation of α into β by means of the family of paths α_v. The function F is not unique, because any continuous family of arcs α_v such that $\alpha_0 = \alpha$ and $\alpha_1 = \beta$ can be used.

This is how we arrive at the mathematical definition of homotopy of simple arcs. Precisely the same method is adopted in the general case, in which the particular space C_1 is replaced by a general space. However, the strict definition of homotopy makes it a relation between mappings rather than between their images. Thus in the case of simple arcs α, β we would not say that the arcs themselves are homotopic, but that the corresponding mappings which define the arcs are homotopic.

In certain circumstances, notably in connection with the fundamental group (which will be defined later), a more restricted type of homotopy is considered. In this some subset of T is required to remain fixed throughout the deformation. Consider, for example, two simple arcs γ, δ in T, having the same end-points x_1 and x_2 (the end-points of an arc are the images of a and b by the mapping from C_1 into T which defines the arc). If γ is deformed continuously into δ by the process described above, but with the additional restriction that each member of the family of intermediate arcs has x_1 and x_2 as its end-points (see figure 17), then we say that the mappings defining γ and

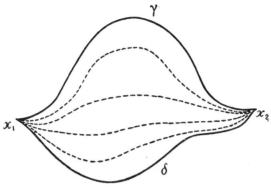

Fig. 17

δ are homotopic relative to the subset of T consisting of x_1 and x_2. In this case the mapping $F : C_1 \times C \to T$ is restricted by the extra conditions $F(a, \ v) = x_1$ and $F(b, \ v) = x_2$ for all values of v such that $0 \leqq v \leqq 1$.

We now give the general definitions of homotopy and homotopy relative to a subset. Let S and T be two topological spaces. If f and g are continuous mappings of S into T, then we say that f is **homotopic** to g, and write $f \frown g$, if there exists a continuous mapping $F : S \times C \to T$ such that $F(x, \ 0) = f(x)$ and $F(x, \ 1) = g(x)$ for every point $x \ \epsilon \ S$. The mapping F is called a **homotopy** of f into g. The notation F_u is used to denote the continuous mapping $F_u : S \to T$ defined by $F_u(x) = F(x, \ u)$, where $x \ \epsilon \ S$. In particular $F_0 = f$ and $F_1 = g$.

Example. If S is a circle and T is a torus, and the images under f and g are the circles C, C' of figure 11, Chapter I, then one homotopy connecting f and g maps a circular cylinder into the shaded region of the torus shown in figure 18. The images of the ends of the cylinder coincide with the images of S by f and g respectively. The images of the other cross-sections are the images by the intermediate mappings F_u, which move continuously from $f(S)$ to $g(S)$.

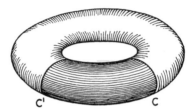

Fig. 18

If f and g are continuous mappings of S into T such that $f(x_0) = g(x_0)$ for each point x_0 in some subset X_0 of S, then we say that f is homotopic to g relative to X_0, and write $f \smile g$ rel X_0, if there is a continuous mapping $F : S \times C \to T$ such that $F(x, 0) = f(x)$ and $F(x, 1) = g(x)$ for each $x \in S$, and also $F(x_0, u) = f(x_0) = g(x_0)$ for each $x_0 \in X_0$. If X_0 is the null set, then $f \smile g$. Thus ordinary homotopy is a particular case of relative homotopy.

32.   Theorems on homotopy.

The following theorem is frequently used in the study of homotopic mappings.

THEOREM 4.1 *If a topological space S is the union of two closed subsets A and B, and if $f : A \to T$ and $g : B \to T$ are continuous mappings of A and B respectively into a space T such that $f(x) = g(x)$ for each element $x \in A \cap B$, then the transformation $h : S \to T$ defined by $h(x) = f(x)$ if $x \in A$ and $h(x) = g(x)$ if $x \in B$, is continuous.*

Proof. Let X be a subset of S. Define $X_1 = X \cap A$ and $X_2 = X \cap B$. Then $X = X_1 \cup X_2$, and so

$$h(X) = h(X_1) \cup h(X_2).$$

By Theorem 2.7 $\overline{X} = \overline{X}_1 \cup \overline{X}_2$. Hence

$$h(\overline{X}) = h(\overline{X}_1) \cup h(\overline{X}_2).$$

Let x be a point of $\overline{X}_1 = \overline{X \cap A}$. Then every open set containing x contains a point of $X \cap A$ and therefore of A; hence $x \in \overline{A}$. But A is closed, and so $x \in A$. Hence $\overline{X}_1 \subset A$, so that $h(\overline{X}_1) = f(\overline{X}_1)$. Similarly $\overline{X}_2 \subset B$, so that $h(\overline{X}_2) = g(\overline{X}_2)$. But f and g are continuous, and so, by Theorem 2.10, $f(\overline{X}_1) \subset \overline{f(X_1)}$ and $g(\overline{X}_2) \subset \overline{g(X_2)}$. Therefore $h(\overline{X}) = h(\overline{X}_1) \cup h(\overline{X}_2) \subset \overline{f(X_1)} \cup \overline{g(X_2)} = \overline{h(X_1)} \cup \overline{h(X_2)}$.

Again using Theorem 2.7,

$$\overline{h(X_1)} \cup \overline{h(X_2)} = \overline{h(X_1) \cup h(X_2)} = \overline{h(X)}.$$

Therefore $h(\overline{X}) \subset \overline{h(X)}$. Hence h is continuous.

THEOREM 4.2 *The relation of being homotopic relative to a subset X_0 is an equivalence relation.*

Proof. We must show that the relation is (1) reflexive, (2) symmetric and (3) transitive.

(1) *Reflexivity.* Define $F(x, u) = f(x)$. Then $F = f \cdot p$, where p is the projection of $S \times C$ onto S, and so, by Theorems 2.6 and 2.14, F is continuous. Clearly $F(x, 0) = f(x) = F(x, 1)$, and $F(x, u) = f(x)$ for any element x of S. Hence $f \smile f$ rel X_0, where X_0 is any subset of S.

(2) *Symmetry.* If $f \smile g$ rel X_0, there exists a continuous mapping $F : S \times C \to T$ such that $F(x, 0) = f(x)$ and $F(x, 1) = g(x)$; also $F(x_0, u) = f(x_0) = g(x_0)$ if $x_0 \in X_0$. Define $G : S \times C \to T$ by $G(x, u) = F(x, 1 - u)$. Then, using Theorem 2.6, G is continuous; also $G(x, 0) = g(x)$, $G(x, 1) = f(x)$ and $G(x_0, u) = f(x_0) = g(x_0)$ if $x_0 \in X_0$. Therefore $g \smile f$ rel X_0.

(3) *Transitivity.* If $f \smile g$ rel X_0 and $g \smile h$ rel X_0, there exist continuous mappings F, $G : S \times C \to T$ such that

$F(x, 0) = f(x)$, $F(x, 1) = g(x)$, $F(x_0, u) = f(x_0) = g(x_0)(x_0 \in X_0)$,
$G(x, 0) = g(x)$, $G(x, 1) = h(x)$, $G(x_0, u) = g(x_0) = h(x_0)(x_0 \in X_0)$.

Define a transformation $H : S \times C \to T$ by

$$H(x, u) = F(x, 2u) \qquad (u \leqq \tfrac{1}{2})$$
$$H(x, u) = G(x, 2u - 1) \quad (u \geqq \tfrac{1}{2}).$$

Then, by Theorem 4.1, H is continuous, and

$H(x, 0) = f(x)$, $H(x, 1) = h(x)$, $H(x_0, u) = f(x_0) = h(x_0)(x_0 \epsilon X_0)$. Therefore $f \backsim h$ rel X_0.

From Theorem 4.2 it follows that the set of all continuous mappings $f : S \to T$ for which the image of a given point $x_0 \epsilon X_0$ is the same point of T can be divided into mutually exclusive classes, such that two mappings are in the same class if and only if they are homotopic rel X_0. These classes of mappings are called **homotopy classes.**

If a mapping $f : S \to T$ is homotopic to a mapping $g : S \to T$ whose image is a single point, so that g is a constant mapping, then f is said to be **homotopic to a constant.** In particular, if the identity $i : S \to S$ is homotopic to a constant, then S is said to be **deformable to a point** or **contractible.**

Example. The unit closed solid n-sphere S_n: that is, the set of points $(x_1, x_2, \ldots, x_n)$ in E_n satisfying $x_1^2 + x_2^2 + \ldots + x_n \leqq 1$, is contractible. For the transformation $F : S_n \times C \to S_n$ defined by $F(x, u) = ((1 - u)x_1, (1 - u)x_2, \ldots, (1 - u)x_n)$, where $x = (x_1, \ldots, x_n)$ is a point of S_n, is continuous; also $F(x, 0) = x$ and $F(x, 1) = (0, 0, \ldots, 0)$. Therefore the identity $i : S_n \to S_n$ is homotopic to a constant.

Intuitively, a contractible space is one which can be deformed over itself into a point. An example of a space which is not contractible is the surface of the sphere, which is not deformable *over itself* into a point.

THEOREM 4.3 *If T is a contractible topological space, every continuous mapping $f : S \to T$ is homotopic to a constant.*

Proof. Since T is contractible, there is a continuous mapping $F : T \times C \to T$ such that $F(y, 0) = y$ and $F(y, 1) = y_0$ where y is an arbitrary element of T and y_0 is a fixed element. Let f be a continuous mapping of S into T. Define $G : S \times C \to T$ by

$$G(x, u) = F(f(x), u) \text{ where } x \epsilon S.$$

Then, making use of Theorem 2.6, G is continuous; also

$G(x, 0) = F(f(x), 0) = f(x)$ and $G(x, 1) = F(f(x), 1) = y_0$. Therefore f is homotopic to the constant transformation $g : S \to T$ defined by $g(x) = y_0$.

Thus, for a contractible space, every continuous mapping into the space is homotopic to a constant. In particular, there is only one homotopy class of mappings of a contractible space into itself.

THEOREM 4.4 *Let f and g be homotopic mappings of T_1 into T_2, and let h be a continuous mapping of T_2 into T_3. Then $h \cdot f$ and $h \cdot g$ are homotopic mappings of T_1 into T_3. Similarly if f' is a continuous mapping of T_1 into T_2, and g' and h' are homotopic mappings of T_2 into T_3, then $g' \cdot f'$ and $h' \cdot f'$ are homotopic mappings of T_1 into T_3.*

Proof. Since $f \smile g$, there is a continuous mapping $F : T_1 \times C \to T_2$ such that $F(x, 0) = f(x)$ and $F(x, 1) = g(x)$, where $x \in T_1$. Define $G : T_1 \times C \to T_3$ by $G(x, u) = h(F(x, u))$. Then, since F and h are continuous, G is continuous, by Theorem 2.6. Also $G(x, 0) = h(F(x, 0)) = h(f(x))$ and $G(x, 1) = h(F(x, 1)) = h(g(x))$. Therefore $h \cdot g \smile h \cdot f$. The second part of the theorem can be proved similarly.

33. Homotopy type. Let S and T be two topological spaces. The space S is said to be of the same **homotopy type** as T if there exist continuous mappings $f : S \to T$ and $g : T \to S$ such that $g \cdot f : S \to S$ is homotopic to the identity $i : S \to S$ and $f \cdot g : T \to T$ is homotopic to the identity $j : T \to T$. Clearly if S is homeomorphic to T, it is of the same homotopy type. But spaces of the same homotopy type need not be homeomorphic. For example a contractible space is of the same homotopy type as a space consisting of a single point; this follows quickly from the definition of contractibility. But a contractible space can only be homeomorphic to a space consisting of a single point if it consists of a single point itself.

The relation of being of the same homotopy type is an equivalence relation. The reflexivity and symmetry follow at once from the definition. To prove that the relation is transitive let T_1, T_2 be of the same homotopy type as T_2 and T_3 respectively. Then there exist continuous mappings $f : T_1 \to T_2$, $g : T_2 \to T_1$, $f' : T_2 \to T_3$, $g' : T_3 \to T_2$ such that $g \cdot f$, $f \cdot g$, $g' \cdot f'$ and $f' \cdot g'$ are homotopic to the appropriate identity mappings. By Theorem 2.6 the transformations $f'' : T_1 \to T_3$ and $g'' : T_3 \to T_1$ defined by $f''(x) = f'(f(x))$ and $g''(x) = g(g'(x))$ are continuous. By Theorem 4.4, $g \cdot (g' \cdot f')$ is homotopic to g, since $g' \cdot f'$ is homotopic to the identity. Hence $g'' \cdot f'' = g \cdot ((g' \cdot f') \cdot f)$ is homotopic to $g \cdot f$, which in its turn is homotopic to the identity. Similarly $f'' \cdot g''$ is homotopic to the identity transformation of T_3 onto itself, and so T_1 is of the same homotopy type as T_3. Therefore the relation is transitive.

It follows that the set of all topological spaces can be separated into mutually exclusive classes according to their homotopy type. These classes are larger than those of topologically equivalent spaces, because topological equivalence is stronger than the equivalence determined by homotopy type. A homotopy invariant, that is something which has the same value for all spaces of the same homotopy type, is necessarily a topological invariant, but a topological invariant need not be a homotopy invariant.

The remainder of this chapter is devoted to a discussion of some of the more important homotopy invariants, namely the fundamental group and the homotopy groups.

34. Paths. A **path** in a topological space T is a continuous mapping $\alpha : C \to T$ of the space C, that is the set of real numbers u satisfying $0 \leqq u \leqq 1$ with the usual topology, into T. The points $\alpha(0)$ and $\alpha(1)$ are called the **beginning** and **end** respectively of the path. The **inverse path** α^{-1} of a given path is defined to be the path given by $\alpha^{-1}(u) = \alpha(1 - u)$. This must not be confused with the inverse of a transformation in the sense of Chapter II, § 9. The inverse of a path will always be taken to be the inverse as just defined. Clearly the end of a path coincides with

the beginning of its inverse, and the beginning of a path
with the end of its inverse. The same set of points in T is
determined by both the path and its inverse, but it is
described in opposite directions.

If $\alpha : C \to T$ and $\beta : C \to T$ are two paths, and if
$\alpha(1) = \beta(0)$, so that the end of α coincides with the beginning of β, then the **product path** $\alpha\beta$ of the paths is defined
to be the path $\gamma : C \to T$ given by

$$\gamma(u) = \alpha(2u) \qquad (0 \leqq u \leqq \tfrac{1}{2})$$
$$\gamma(u) = \beta(2u - 1) \quad (\tfrac{1}{2} \leqq u \leqq 1).$$

The function γ defined in this way is continuous by Theorem 4.1, and, since it maps C into T, it is therefore a path
in T. The product of two paths defined in this way must
not be confused with the product of two functions as
defined in Chapter II, § 9. Intuitively, $\alpha\beta$ can be thought
of as the path α followed by the path β.

A path α for which $\alpha(C)$ is a single element of T, so that
α is a constant mapping, is called a **null path.**

A path α is called **closed** if its end coincides with its
beginning, so that $\alpha(0) = \alpha(1)$. For example $\alpha\alpha^{-1}$ and
$\alpha^{-1}\alpha$ are closed paths.

If α and β are two paths in T which have the same
beginning and the same end, so that $\alpha(0) = \beta(0)$ and
$\alpha(1) = \beta(1)$, then α is said to be **homotopic** to β, written
$\alpha \smallfrown \beta$, if α is homotopic to β relative to the subset of C
which consists of the points $u = 0$ and $u = 1$. (We recall
that paths are, by definition, continuous mappings, so that
the definition of § 31 can be applied).

The following theorems, except for Theorem 4.10, will
be used later in verifying the group properties of the fundamental group. The properties proved are 'obvious'
geometrically, and, while rigorous proofs must be of an
analytical nature, the geometrical pictures are useful as
guides in constructing the proofs.

THEOREM 4.5 *If α, β, γ, δ are paths such that $\alpha \smallfrown \gamma$ and
$\beta \smallfrown \delta$, and if $\alpha\beta$ exists, then $\gamma\delta$ exists and $\alpha\beta \smallfrown \gamma\delta$.*

Proof. Since $\alpha\beta$ is defined, $\alpha(1) = \beta(0)$. Since $\alpha \frown \gamma$ and $\beta \frown \delta$, $\alpha(1) = \gamma(1)$ and $\beta(0) = \delta(0)$. Therefore $\gamma(1) = \delta(0)$, and so $\gamma\delta$ exists. Since $\alpha \frown \gamma$, there is a continuous mapping $F : C \times C \to T$ such that

$$F(u, 0) = \alpha(u), \qquad F(u, 1) = \gamma(u),$$
$$F(0, v) = \alpha(0) = \gamma(0), \quad F(1, v) = \alpha(1) = \gamma(1).$$

Similarly, since $\beta \frown \delta$, there is a continuous mapping $G : C \times C \to T$ such that

$$G(u, 0) = \beta(u), \qquad G(u, 1) = \delta(u),$$
$$G(0, v) = \beta(0) = \delta(0), \quad G(1, v) = \beta(1) = \delta(1).$$

Define $H : C \times C \to T$ by

$$H(u, v) = F(2u, v) \qquad (0 \leqq u \leqq \tfrac{1}{2}),$$
$$H(u, v) = G(2u - 1, v) \quad (\tfrac{1}{2} \leqq u \leqq 1).$$

Then, by Theorem 4.1, H is continuous; and

$$H(u, 0) = \alpha(2u) \qquad (0 \leqq u \leqq \tfrac{1}{2}),$$
$$H(u, 0) = \beta(2u - 1) \qquad (\tfrac{1}{2} \leqq u \leqq 1),$$
$$H(u, 1) = \gamma(2u) \qquad (0 \leqq u \leqq \tfrac{1}{2}),$$
$$H(u, 1) = \delta(2u - 1) \qquad (\tfrac{1}{2} \leqq u \leqq 1),$$
$$H(0, v) = F(0, v) = \alpha(0) = \gamma(0),$$
$$H(1, v) = G(1, v) = \beta(1) = \delta(1).$$

Therefore $\alpha\beta \frown \gamma\delta$.

THEOREM 4.6 *If α and β are paths such that $\alpha \frown \beta$, then $\alpha^{-1} \frown \beta^{-1}$.*

Proof. If $\alpha \frown \beta$, there is a continuous mapping $F : C \times C \to T$ such that

$$F(u, 0) = \alpha(u), \; F(u, 1) = \beta(u),$$
$$F(0, v) = \alpha(0) = \beta(0),$$
$$F(1, v) = \alpha(1) = \beta(1).$$

Define $G : C \times C \to T$ by $G(u, v) = F(1 - u, v)$. Then G is continuous, and

$$G(u, 0) = \alpha(1 - u), \; G(u, 1) = \beta(1 - u),$$
$$G(0, v) = F(1, v) = \alpha(1) = \beta(1),$$
$$G(1, v) = F(0, v) = \alpha(0) = \beta(0).$$

Therefore $\alpha^{-1} \frown \beta^{-1}$.

THEOREM 4.7 *If α is any path, and β is a null path such that $\alpha\beta$ exists, then $\alpha\beta \smile \alpha$. Similarly, if γ is a null path such that $\gamma\alpha$ exists, then $\gamma\alpha \smile \alpha$.*

Proof. Since $\alpha\beta$ exists and β is a null path, $\beta(u) = \alpha(1)$. Define $F : C \times C \to T$ by

$$F(u, v) = \alpha(2u/(1 + v)) \quad (0 \leqq u \leqq \tfrac{1}{2}(1 + v)),$$
$$F(u, v) = \alpha(1) \quad\quad\quad (\tfrac{1}{2}(1 + v) \leqq u \leqq 1).$$

Then

$$F(u, 0) = \alpha(2u) \quad (0 \leqq u \leqq \tfrac{1}{2}),$$
$$F(u, 0) = \alpha(1) \quad\;\; (\tfrac{1}{2} \leqq u \leqq 1),$$
$$F(0, v) = \alpha(0), \quad F(1, v) = \alpha(1),$$

and F is continuous. Therefore $\alpha\beta \smile \alpha$. Similarly $\gamma\alpha \smile \alpha$.

THEOREM 4.8 *If α, β and γ are three paths such that $\alpha\beta$ and $\beta\gamma$ exist, then $(\alpha\beta)\gamma$ and $\alpha(\beta\gamma)$ both exist and $(\alpha\beta)\gamma \smile \alpha(\beta\gamma)$.*

Proof. The transformation $F : C \times C \to T$ defined by

$$F(u, v) = \alpha(4u/(1 + v)) \quad (0 \leqq u \leqq \tfrac{1}{4}(1 + v)),$$
$$F(u, v) = \beta(4u - 1 - v) \quad (\tfrac{1}{4}(1 + v) \leqq u \leqq \tfrac{1}{4}(2 + v)),$$
$$F(u, v) = \gamma(1 - 4(1 - u)/(2 - v)) \quad (\tfrac{1}{4}(2 + v) \leqq u \leqq 1),$$

is continuous, by Theorem 4.1. Also

$$F(u, 0) = \alpha(4u) \quad\quad (0 \leqq u \leqq \tfrac{1}{4}),$$
$$F(u, 0) = \beta(4u - 1) \quad (\tfrac{1}{4} \leqq u \leqq \tfrac{1}{2}),$$
$$F(u, 0) = \gamma(2u - 1) \quad (\tfrac{1}{2} \leqq u \leqq 1),$$
$$F(u, 1) = \alpha(2u) \quad\quad (0 \leqq u \leqq \tfrac{1}{2}),$$
$$F(u, 1) = \beta(4u - 2) \quad (\tfrac{1}{2} \leqq u \leqq \tfrac{3}{4}),$$
$$F(u, 1) = \gamma(4u - 3) \quad (\tfrac{3}{4} \leqq u \leqq 1).$$

Hence $F(u, 0) = \delta_0(u)$, where $\delta_0 = (\alpha\beta)\gamma$, and $F(u, 1) = \delta_1(u)$, where $\delta_1 = \alpha(\beta\gamma)$. Also

$$F(0, v) = \alpha(0) = \delta_0(0),$$
$$F(1, v) = \gamma(1) = \delta_1(1).$$

Therefore $(\alpha\beta)\gamma \smile \alpha(\beta\gamma)$.

THEOREM 4.9 *If α is any path, then $\alpha\alpha^{-1}$ and $\alpha^{-1}\alpha$ are homotopic to null paths.*

Proof. Define $F : C \times C \to T$ by

$$F(u, v) = \alpha(2u(1 - v)) \qquad (0 \leqq u \leqq \tfrac{1}{2}),$$
$$F(u, v) = \alpha(2(1 - u)(1 - v)) \quad (\tfrac{1}{2} \leqq u \leqq 1).$$

Then F is continuous, and

$$F(u, 0) = \alpha(2u) \qquad (0 \leqq u \leqq \tfrac{1}{2}),$$
$$F(u, 0) = \alpha(2 - 2u) \quad (\tfrac{1}{2} \leqq u \leqq 1),$$
$$F(u, 1) = \alpha(0),$$
$$F(0, v) = \alpha(0) = F(1, v).$$

Therefore $\alpha\alpha^{-1}$ is homotopic to the null path whose image is $\alpha(0)$. Similarly, $\alpha^{-1}\alpha$ is homotopic to the null path whose image is $\alpha(1)$.

THEOREM 4.10 *Let α and β be two paths such that $\alpha\beta^{-1}$ exists and is a closed path. Then $\alpha\beta^{-1}$ is homotopic to a null path if and only if $\alpha \frown \beta$.*

Proof. Since $\alpha\beta^{-1}$ exists, $\alpha(1) = \beta(1)$, and since $\alpha\beta^{-1}$ is closed, $\alpha(0) = \beta(0)$. Suppose that $\alpha\beta^{-1}$ is homotopic to a null path. Then, by Theorems 4.5 and 4.7, $(\alpha\beta^{-1})\beta$ is homotopic to β. But, by Theorem 4.8, $(\alpha\beta^{-1})\beta$ is homotopic to $\alpha(\beta^{-1}\beta)$, which, by Theorems 4.9 and 4.7, is homotopic to α. Hence $\alpha \frown \beta$.

Conversely, suppose that $\alpha \frown \beta$. Then, by Theorem 4.5, $\alpha\beta^{-1} \frown \beta\beta^{-1}$, and, by Theorem 4.9, $\beta\beta^{-1}$ is homotopic to a null path. Hence $\alpha\beta^{-1}$ is homotopic to a null path.

35. The fundamental group. Let T be a topological space, and let x_0 be a fixed point of T. Consider the set of all closed paths which begin and end at x_0. The point x_0 is called the **base point** for the paths, and the paths are referred to as 'paths at x_0'. If α is a path at x_0, we denote the class of all paths at x_0 homotopic to α by $[\alpha]$. Multiplication of these classes of paths is defined by the rule

$$[\alpha][\beta] = [\alpha\beta].$$

By Theorem 4.5 this definition is independent of the choice of representatives of $[\alpha]$ and $[\beta]$, for if $\alpha \frown \gamma$ and $\beta \frown \delta$, then $\alpha\beta \frown \gamma\delta$, and so $[\gamma][\delta] = [\gamma\delta] = [\alpha\beta]$. Thus the product $[\alpha][\beta]$ is uniquely defined by $[\alpha]$ and $[\beta]$.

Using the theorems of § 34, we now show that this operation defines a group structure in the set of homotopy classes of paths at x_0. We verify the four conditions for a group given in Chapter II, § 25.

(i) The product $[\alpha][\beta]$ is a homotopy class of paths at x_0, by definition.

(ii) $([\alpha][\beta])[\gamma] = [\alpha\beta][\gamma] = [(\alpha\beta)\gamma],$
$[\alpha]([\beta][\gamma]) = [\alpha][\beta\gamma] = [\alpha(\beta\gamma)].$

But, by Theorem 4.8, $(\alpha\beta)\gamma \smallfrown \alpha(\beta\gamma)$. Therefore the operation satisfies the associative law.

(iii) Let $[1]$ denote the homotopy class of the null path at x_0. Then, by Theorem 4.7, $[\alpha][1] = [\alpha] = [1][\alpha]$. Thus $[1]$ is a unit element.

(iv) By Theorem 4.9, $[\alpha][\alpha^{-1}] = [\alpha\alpha^{-1}] = [1]$. Thus each element possesses an inverse.

Thus the set of all homotopy classes of paths beginning and ending at x_0, with multiplication defined in this way, is a group. This group is called the **fundamental group** at x_0. It is denoted by $\pi_1(T, x_0)$.

An **isomorphism** Φ between two groups G_1, G_2 is a one-one transformation $\Phi : G_1 \to G_2$ of G_1 *onto* G_2 which preserves the group operation. Thus $\Phi(gh) = \Phi(g)\Phi(h)$ for any pair of elements of G_1. We now show that the fundamental groups at any two points of an arc-wise connected space are isomorphic. Thus, for such spaces, the fundamental group is essentially independent of the base point.

THEOREM 4.11 *If T is an arc-wise connected topological space, and x_0, x_1 are any two points of T, then $\pi_1(T, x_0)$ is isomorphic with $\pi_1(T, x_1)$.*

Proof. Let α be a closed path at $x_0 \in T$. Since T is arc-wise connected, there is a path in T for which x_0 is the beginning and x_1 is the end. Let γ be such a path. Then $\beta = (\gamma^{-1}\alpha)\gamma$ is a closed path beginning and ending at x_1. We define a transformation Φ of the homotopy classes of paths at x_0 into the homotopy classes of paths at x_1 by $\Phi[\alpha] = [\beta]$. Then $\Phi[\alpha]$ is uniquely determined by $[\alpha]$.

F

Conversely $[\alpha]$ is uniquely determined by $\Phi[\alpha]$, for if $(\gamma^{-1}\alpha_1)\gamma \smallsmile (\gamma^{-1}\alpha_2)\gamma$, then $\alpha_1 \smallsmile \alpha_2$ by Theorems 4.8 and 4.9. Moreover, given any path β at x_1, β is homotopic to $\gamma^{-1}((\gamma\beta)\gamma^{-1})\gamma$ and so every homotopy class of paths at x_1 is of the form $\Phi[\alpha]$ for some $[\alpha]$. Thus Φ is a one-one transformation of the elements of $\pi_1(T, x_0)$ onto the elements of $\pi_1(T, x_1)$. If $[\alpha_1]$ and $[\alpha_2]$ are two elements of $\pi_1(T, x_0)$, then

$$\Phi[\alpha_1]\Phi[\alpha_2] = ((\gamma^{-1}\alpha_1)\gamma)((\gamma^{-1}\alpha_2)\gamma) = \Phi[\alpha_1\alpha_2]$$

by Theorems 4.8 and 4.9. Therefore Φ is an isomorphism.

We now examine the relationships between the fundamental groups of different spaces. We first consider the effect of a continuous transformation of a given space. The fundamental group of the image of the transformation need not be isomorphic to the fundamental group of the original space; however, there is a relationship between the structures of the groups. In fact, there is a **homomorphism** between the groups (not to be confused with homeomorphism). A homomorphism between a group G_1 and a group G_2 is a many-one transformation $\Phi : G_1 \rightarrow G_2$ of G_1 into G_2 such that $\Phi(gh) = \Phi(g)\Phi(h)$ for every pair of elements g, h of G_1. Comparing this with the definition of isomorphism, we see that an isomorphism is a one-one homomorphism of G_1 onto G_2.

THEOREM 4.12 *If* $f : T_1 \rightarrow T_2$ *is a continuous transformation of* T_1 *into* T_2, *then there exists a homomorphism* $f^* : \pi_1(T_1, x_0) \rightarrow \pi_1(T_2, f(x_0))$, *where* x_0 *is any point of* T_1.

Proof. Let α, β be closed paths at the point $x_0 \in T_1$. Define γ, $\delta : C \rightarrow T_2$ by $\gamma = f . \alpha$ and $\delta = f . \beta$ respectively; thus $\gamma(u) = f . \alpha(u)$ and $\delta(u) = f . \beta(u)$. Then γ and δ are closed paths in T_2, with base point $f(x_0)$.

If $\alpha \smallsmile \beta$, there exists a continuous mapping $F : C \times C \rightarrow T_1$ such that

$$F(u, 0) = \alpha(u),$$
$$F(u, 1) = \beta(u),$$

$$F(0, v) = \alpha(0) = \beta(0) = x_0,$$
$$F(1, v) = \alpha(1) = \beta(1) = x_0.$$

Define $G : C \times C \to T_2$ by $G(u, v) = f(F(u, v))$. Then, by Theorem 2.6, G is continuous. Moreover

$$G(u, 0) = f \cdot \alpha(u) = \gamma(u),$$
$$G(u, 1) = f \cdot \beta(u) = \delta(u),$$
$$G(0, v) = f(x_0),$$
$$G(1, v) = f(x_0).$$

Therefore $\gamma \smile \delta$.

Therefore, if we define $f^*[\alpha] = [f \cdot \alpha]$, then f^* is a transformation of homotopy classes of paths in T_1 at x_0 into homotopy classes of paths in T_2 at $f(x_0)$ such that $f^*[\alpha]$ is uniquely defined by $[\alpha]$. This transformation is said to be **induced** by f. Thus, with each element of $\pi_1(T_1, x_0)$, the induced transformation f^* associates a unique element of $\pi_1(T_2, f(x_0))$.

Let α, β be two paths in T_1 at x_0, and let $\gamma = f \cdot \alpha$ and $\delta = f \cdot \beta$ be the corresponding paths in T_2. Then $\alpha\beta$ is the path $\rho : C \to T_1$ defined by

$$\rho(u) = \alpha(2u) \qquad (0 \leq u \leq \tfrac{1}{2}),$$
$$\rho(u) = \beta(2u - 1) \qquad (\tfrac{1}{2} \leq u \leq 1).$$

Therefore $f \cdot \rho$ is the path $\sigma : C \to T_2$ defined by

$$\sigma(u) = f(\alpha(2u)) \qquad (0 \leq u \leq \tfrac{1}{2}),$$
$$\sigma(u) = f(\beta(2u - 1)) \ (\tfrac{1}{2} \leq u \leq 1),$$

which is in fact the path $\gamma\delta$. Therefore

$$f^*[\alpha]f^*[\beta] = [\gamma][\delta] = [\gamma\delta] = f^*[\alpha\beta].$$

Hence f^* is a homomorphism of $\pi_1(T_1, x_0)$ into $\pi_1(T_2, f(x_0))$.

We now show that, under certain conditions, the homomorphism of Theorem 4.12 becomes an isomorphism. In particular if f is a homeomorphism, f^* is an isomorphism. This will be proved as a corollary to a more general theorem, which in its turn is a particular case of the theorem (which we shall not prove) that two spaces of the same homotopy type have isomorphic fundamental groups.

THEOREM 4.13 *If T_1 and T_2 are topological spaces such that there exist continuous mappings $f : T_1 \to T_2$ and $g : T_2 \to T_1$ satisfying* (1) $g(y_0) = x_0$, *where $y_0 = f(x_0)$ and x_0 is some fixed point of T_1,* (2) $g \cdot f$ *is homotopic rel x_0 to the identity $i : T_1 \to T_1$,* (3) $f \cdot g$ *is homotopic rel y_0 to the identity $j : T_2 \to T_2$, then $\pi_1(T_1, x_0)$ is isomorphic with $\pi_1(T_2, y_0)$.*

Proof. By Theorem 4.12, the mappings f, g, $g \cdot f$ and $f \cdot g$ induce homomorphisms $f^* : \pi_1(T_1, x_0) \to \pi_1(T_2, y_0)$, $g^* : \pi_1(T_2, y_0) \to \pi_1(T_1, x_0)$, $(gf)^* : \pi_1(T_1, x_0) \to \pi_1(T_1, x_0)$ and $(fg)^* : \pi_1(T_2, y_0) \to \pi_1(T_2, y_0)$ respectively.

Let α be any path in T_1 with base point x_0. Then $(g \cdot f) \cdot \alpha$ is also a path in T_1 with base point x_0, since $g \cdot f(x_0) = g(y_0) = x_0$. But $g \cdot f$ is homotopic rel x_0 to the identity $i : T_1 \to T_1$, and therefore $(g \cdot f) \cdot \alpha$ is homotopic to α. Hence $(g \cdot f)^*$ is the identity transformation of $\pi_1(T_1, x_0)$ onto itself. Similarly $(f \cdot g)^*$ is the identity transformation of $\pi_1(T_2, y_0)$ onto itself.

Consider the path $(g \cdot f) \cdot \alpha : C \to T_1$. This is identical with $g \cdot (f \cdot \alpha) : C \to T_1$. Therefore, if $f^*[\alpha] = [\beta]$, then $g^*[\beta] = (g \cdot f)^*[\alpha]$; symbolically $(g \cdot f)^* = g^* \cdot f^*$. Similarly $(f \cdot g)^* = f^* \cdot g^*$. Therefore $g^* \cdot f^*$ and $f^* \cdot g^*$ are the identity transformations of $\pi_1(T_1, x_0)$ and $\pi_1(T_2, y_0)$ respectively.

Since $f^*[\alpha] = [\beta]$, then $g^* \cdot f^*[\alpha] = g^*[\beta]$, and so $[\alpha] = g^*[\beta]$. If $f^*[\alpha_1] = f^*[\alpha_2]$, then $[\beta_1] = [\beta_2]$ and so $[\alpha_1] = [\alpha_2]$. Therefore f^* is a one-one transformation. Similarly g^* is a one-one transformation. Moreover every element of $\pi_1(T_2, y_0)$ is of the form $f^*[\gamma]$ for some element $[\gamma]$ of $\pi_1(T_1, x_0)$. Hence f^* is a one-one homomorphism of $\pi_1(T_1, x_0)$ onto $\pi_1(T_2, y_0)$, and so it is an isomorphism; similarly g^* is an isomorphism of $\pi_1(T_2, y_0)$ onto $\pi_1(T_1, x_0)$.

COROLLARY. *If T_1 is homeomorphic with T_2, then $\pi_1(T_1, x_0)$ is isomorphic with $\pi_1(T_2, y_0)$, where y_0 is the image of x_0 under the homeomorphism.*

To prove this, we choose $f : T_1 \to T_2$ to be a homeomorphism, and g to be f^{-1}.

Example 1. *The sphere.* The fundamental group of the sphere consists of a single element, the identity, because all closed paths are homotopic to a null path.

In general, a space whose fundamental group consists of a single element, the identity alone, is called **simply connected.**

Example 2. *The circle.* Let P be any point on the circle. Then a closed path which begins and ends at P is homotopic to either a null path or one given by one or more complete descriptions of the circle. Suppose α is a path which describes the circle r times, and β is a path which describes it s times. Then, if $r > s$, α is not homotopic to β, for $\alpha\beta^{-1}$ is a path describing the circle $r - s$ times, and such a path is not homotopic to a null path. Thus the homotopy classes of paths are in one-one correspondence with the additive group of integers, and it is easily seen that this correspondence is an isomorphism. Thus the fundamental group of the circle is an infinite cyclic group: that is, a group consisting of the identity and the integral powers of a fixed element.

Example 3. *The torus.* There are infinitely many homotopy classes of paths beginning and ending at a point P of the torus, for two paths of the type shown in figure 19 are not homotopic if they complete different numbers of circuits of the torus. The fundamental group in this case is a commutative group on two generators: that is, it consists of elements of the form $g_1^r g_2^s$ where g_1 and g_2 are two fixed elements such that $g_1 g_2 = g_2 g_1$, and r and s are positive integers.

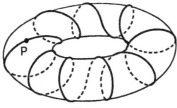

Fig. 19

The elements g_1 and g_2 correspond to the paths C_1 and C_2 (the meridian and parallel through P) shown in figure 20, in which the torus is represented by a rectangle with opposite sides identified. The fact that $g_1 g_2 = g_2 g_1$ corresponds to the fact that $C_1 C_2$ is homotopic to $C_2 C_1$. The paths C' and C'' in figure 20 are typical members of a family of paths by means of which $C_1 C_2$ can be deformed continuously into $C_2 C_1$.

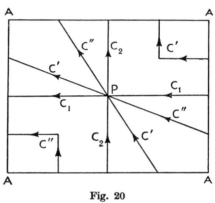

Fig. 20

In the above examples, the fundamental groups are commutative. However, this property is not true in general. For example the fundamental group of the double torus is non-commutative.

36. The Homotopy Groups. The elements of the fundamental group are homotopy classes of paths, which are regarded as one-dimensional because they are mappings of a portion of the Euclidean line. The homotopy groups are generalisations of this to any dimension $n > 1$. For the sake of simplicity, we define only the absolute homotopy groups and not the more general relative homotopy groups.

The n-dimensional cube I_n is the subset of points $(u_1, u_2, \ldots, u_n)$ in Euclidean space E_n satisfying $0 \leq u_i \leq 1$ $(i = 1, 2, \ldots, n)$, together with the usual topology. The boundary J_n of I_n is the union of all the subsets of I_n for which one of the coordinates u_i is restricted to be either 0 or 1. Thus, if $n = 2$, I_2 consists of the interior and edges of a unit square and J_2 is the perimeter of the square.

Let T be any topological space, and let α, β be continuous mappings of I_n into T such that $\alpha(J_n)=x_0=\beta(J_n)$, where x_0 is a fixed point of T. If $n = 1$, α and β are closed paths in T with base point x_0. Define a transformation $\gamma : I_n \to T$ by

$$\gamma(u_1, \ldots, u_n) = \alpha(2u_1, u_2, \ldots, u_n) \qquad (0 \leqq u_1 \leqq \tfrac{1}{2}),$$
$$\gamma(u_1, \ldots, u_n) = \beta(2u_1 - 1, u_2, \ldots, u_n) \qquad (\tfrac{1}{2} \leqq u_1 \leqq 1).$$

Then, by Theorem 4.1, γ is continuous. Also $\gamma(J_n) = x_0$. Thus, if $n = 1$, γ is the product of the paths α and β as defined in § 34. If $n > 1$, we define $\gamma = \alpha + \beta$. (The additive notation is appropriate only when $n > 1$).

Suppose now that α, β, γ, δ are continuous mappings of I_n $(n > 1)$ into T such that the image of J_n by each mapping is x_0. If $\alpha \smallfrown \gamma$ rel J_n, there exists a continuous mapping $F : I_n \times C \to T$ such that

$$F(u_1, \ldots, u_n, 0) = \alpha(u_1, \ldots, u_n),$$
$$F(u_1, \ldots, u_n, 1) = \gamma(u_1, \ldots, u_n),$$
$$F(\dot{u}_1, \ldots, \dot{u}_n, v) = x_0$$

where $(\dot{u}_1, \ldots, \dot{u}_n) \epsilon J_n$. Similarly, if $\beta \smallfrown \delta$ rel J_n, there exists a continuous mapping $G : I_n \times C \to T$ which agrees with β when $v = 0$, with δ when $v = 1$, and is such that $G(J_n \times C) = x_0$. Defining $H : I_n \times C \to T$ by

$$H(u_1, \ldots, u_n, v) = F(2u_1, \ldots, u_n, v) \qquad (0 \leqq u_1 \leqq \tfrac{1}{2})$$
$$H(u_1, \ldots, u_n, v) = G(2u_1 - 1, \ldots, u_n, v) \qquad (\tfrac{1}{2} \leqq u_1 \leqq 1)$$

we obtain a continuous mapping H such that

$$H(u_1, \ldots, u_n, 0) = (\alpha + \beta)(u_1, \ldots, u_n)$$
$$H(u_1, \ldots, u_n, 1) = (\gamma + \delta)(u_1, \ldots, u_n)$$
$$H(\dot{u}_1, \ldots, \dot{u}_n, v) = x_0.$$

Thus, if $\alpha \smallfrown \gamma$ rel J_n and $\beta \smallfrown \delta$ rel J_n, then $\alpha + \beta \smallfrown \gamma + \delta$ rel J_n.

Consider the set of all homotopy classes rel J_n of continuous mappings $\alpha : I_n \to T$ such that $\alpha(J_n) = x_0$. If n is a fixed integer > 1, we define the sum of two such classes $[\alpha]$ and $[\beta]$ by

$$[\alpha] + [\beta] = [\alpha + \beta].$$

This sum is uniquely defined by $[\alpha]$ and $[\beta]$, for, as we have shown, if $\alpha \frown \gamma$ rel J_n and $\beta \frown \delta$ rel J_n, then $\alpha + \beta \frown \gamma + \delta$ rel J_n. With respect to addition defined in this way, the set of homotopy classes forms, for each integer $n > 1$, a group $\pi_n(T, x_0)$. This group is called the **n-dimensional homotopy group** of T at x_0. To complete the definition, the fundamental group is called the one-dimensional homotopy group.

The group properties of $\pi_n(T, x_0)$ can be verified in the same way as for the fundamental group. If T is an arcwise connected topological space, it can be shown that $\pi_n(T, x_0)$ is isomorphic with $\pi_n(T, x_1)$ for any two points x_0 and x_1 of T. It can also be shown that the homotopy groups are invariants of homotopy type, so that two spaces of the same homotopy type have isomorphic homotopy groups. A weaker theorem was proved above (Theorem 4.13) in the case $n = 1$. A corollary to the general theorem is that homeomorphic spaces have isomorphic homotopy groups.

Though the fundamental group need not be commutative, the groups $\pi_n(T, x_0)$ are, for $n > 1$, all commutative. This accounts for our use of the additive notation in the case $n > 1$. For a proof of the commutativity, and for further information regarding homotopy groups (particularly concerning the difficult problem of computing the groups), the reader is referred to P. J. Hilton's *An Introduction to Homotopy Theory*, and N. E. Steenrod's *The Topology of Fibre Bundles*.

Exercises.

(1). Let x and y be points of the topological spaces S and T respectively. Show that $\pi_1(S \times T, (x, y))$ is isomorphic with the direct product of the groups $\pi_1(S, x)$ and $\pi_1(T, y)$.

(2). Show that the fundamental group of the real projective plane is a cyclic group of order two. (Use the representation given by figure 10 in Chapter I).

CHAPTER V

SIMPLICIAL COMPLEXES

37. Introduction. Algebraic topology is the subject of this chapter and the next. The main concern of algebraic topology is the idea of homology (and its dual, cohomology), which arose out of Poincaré's attempts to classify manifolds (topological spaces such that every point lies in an open set homeomorphic with a neighbourhood of a point in Euclidean space) in terms of a calculable set of invariants. The invariants provided by homology theory can in many cases be calculated without much difficulty, but so far they have proved to be inadequate for the required classification.

The idea behind elementary homology theory is that of triangulation, which is the process of dividing up a space into pieces which are homeomorphic with the interior of a triangle or its analogues in other dimensions. The purpose of this chapter is to introduce the idea of triangulation by means of simplicial complexes. Homology itself is the subject of the next chapter.

38. Linear subspaces of Euclidean space. Let P_α ($\alpha = 0, 1, \ldots, m$) be $m + 1$ points in n-dimensional Euclidean space E_n, with $n > m$ and let the coordinates of P_α be $p_{\alpha i}$ ($i = 1, \ldots, n$). The points $P_0, \ldots, P_m$ are said to be **linearly independent** if the equations

$$\sum_{\alpha=0}^{m} a_\alpha p_{\alpha i} = 0, \quad \sum_{\alpha=0}^{m} a_\alpha = 0$$

imply that $a_\alpha = 0$ for all α, the a_α being real numbers †.

† See, for example, A. C. Aitken's *Determinants and Matrices*, § 27.

If $P_0, \ldots, P_m$ are linearly independent, then the $n + 1$ by $m + 1$ matrix whose i^{th} row is $(p_{0i}, \ldots, p_{mi})$ for $i = 1, \ldots, n$ and whose last row is $(1, 1, \ldots, 1)$, is of rank $m + 1$. Hence the equations

$$\sum_{i=1}^{n} p_{\alpha i} h_i = k$$

have $n - m$ linearly independent solutions for $h_1, h_2, \ldots, h_n$, k, and so the points P_α satisfy $n - m$ independent equations of this form. For example, if $n = 3$ and $m = 2$, we have three linearly independent points. They satisfy a single linear equation, and so define a plane in E_3. If $n = 3$ and $m = 1$, we have two linearly independent points which satisfy two linear equations and define a line in E_3.

A **linear subspace** L of E_n is a subset of E_n such that, if the points $P = (x_i)$ and $Q = (y_i)$ are in L, then so are the points $\lambda P + \mu Q$ for which $\lambda + \mu = 1$; here $\lambda P + \mu Q$ denotes the point whose coordinates are $(\lambda x_i + \mu y_i)$.

The set of points $X = (x_i)$ such that, for some real numbers t_α,

$$x_i = \sum_{\alpha=0}^{m} t_\alpha p_{\alpha i} \text{ where } \sum_{\alpha=0}^{m} t_\alpha = 1,$$

form a linear subspace of E_n. For, if X and X' are two such points, and $\lambda + \mu = 1$, then

$$\lambda x_i + \mu x_i' = \sum_{\alpha=0}^{m} (\lambda t_\alpha p_{\alpha i} + \mu t_\alpha' p_{\alpha i})$$

$$= \sum_{\alpha=0}^{m} (\lambda t_\alpha + \mu t_\alpha') p_{\alpha i}$$

and

$$\sum_{\alpha=0}^{m} (\lambda t_\alpha + \mu t_\alpha') = \lambda \sum_{\alpha=0}^{m} t_\alpha + \mu \sum_{\alpha=0}^{m} t_\alpha' = \lambda + \mu = 1,$$

so that $\lambda X + \mu X'$ is of the required form. Moreover this linear subspace contains all the points $P_0, \ldots, P_m$. In fact, P_α is given by $t_\beta = 0$ ($\beta \neq \alpha$) and $t_\alpha = 1$. The subspace is therefore called the linear subspace **spanned** by $P_0, P_1, \ldots, P_m$.

The numbers t_α are called the **barycentric coordinates** of the point X referred to the points P_α. Clearly there is a one-one correspondence between the set of points in the subspace spanned by $P_0, P_1, \ldots, P_m$ and their barycentric coordinates. For, if the t's are given, then $x_i = \sum_{\alpha=0}^{m} t_\alpha p_{\alpha i}$ is uniquely defined, and conversely if $\sum t_\alpha p_{\alpha i} = \sum t'_\alpha p_{\alpha i}$ then $t_\alpha = t'_\alpha$ because the P_α are independent.

In the case $m = 1$, the barycentric coordinates are the parameters in Joachimsthal's ratio equations. In the case $m = 2$, they are areal coordinates referred to the triangle $P_0 P_1 P_2$ as triangle of reference.

A **convex linear subspace** of E_n is a subset of E_n such that, if $P = (x_i)$ and $Q = (y_i)$ are in the set, then so is the point $\lambda P + \mu Q$, where $\lambda + \mu = 1$ and λ, μ are both non-negative. Thus if a convex linear subspace contains the points P and Q it contains the segment of the line PQ joining P and Q. For example, the interior of a circle or a square is a convex linear subspace in E_3. Other examples of convex linear subspaces are the subsets of the linear subspace spanned by $m + 1$ linearly independent points whose barycentric coordinates satisfy $0 < t_\alpha < 1$ or alternatively $0 \leq t_\alpha \leq 1$.

39. Simplexes. A **geometric m-simplex** σ^m ($m > 0$) is a set of points $X = (x_i)$ defined in terms of $m + 1$ linearly independent points $P_0, P_1, \ldots, P_m$ by

$$x_i = \sum_{\alpha=0}^{m} t_\alpha p_{\alpha i} \quad (i = 1, \ldots, n),$$

where $\sum_{\alpha=0}^{m} t_\alpha = 1$ and $0 < t_\alpha < 1$ ($\alpha = 0, 1, \ldots, m$). Thus it is a convex linear subspace in the linear subspace spanned by $P_0, \ldots, P_m$. A **geometric 0-simplex** σ^0 is simply a point. The number m is called the **dimension** of the simplex.

In the cases $m = 1, 2, 3$ a geometric m-simplex is an open interval, the interior of a triangle and the interior of a tetrahedron respectively.

A geometric m-simplex is sometimes called an **open geometric m-simplex** to distinguish it from a **closed geometric m-simplex** which is defined in the same way, except that the conditions $0 < t_\alpha < 1$ are replaced by $0 \leq t_\alpha \leq 1$. If σ^m denotes a given open geometric m-simplex, the corresponding closed geometric m-simplex is denoted by $\overline{\sigma}^m$. When the Euclidean space has the usual topology, $\overline{\sigma}^m$ is just the closure of σ^m.

A **q-face** $(q \leq m)$ of a geometric m-simplex σ^m is a subset of $\overline{\sigma}^m$ whose points X satisfy

$$x_i = \sum_{\alpha=0}^{m} t_\alpha p_{\alpha i}, \quad \sum_{\alpha=0}^{m} t_\alpha = 1,$$

$$0 < t_{\alpha_0} < 1, \; 0 < t_{\alpha_1} < 1, \ldots, 0 < t_{\alpha_q} < 1.$$

$$t_{\alpha_{q+1}} = 0 = \ldots = t_{\alpha_m},$$

where $\alpha_0, \alpha_1, \ldots, \alpha_m$ are the integers $0, 1, \ldots, m$ in some order. Thus a q-face is a geometric q-simplex, for if we write $t'_\beta = t_{\alpha_\beta}$ and $P'_\beta = P_{\alpha_\beta}$ the q-face is determined completely by

$$x_i = \sum_{\alpha=0}^{q} t'_\alpha p'_{\alpha i}, \quad \sum_{\alpha=0}^{q} t'_\alpha = 1, \quad 0 < t'_\alpha < 1.$$

The 0-faces of σ^m consist of the points $P_0, P_1, \ldots, P_m$, which are called the **vertices** of the simplex. The 1-faces are called the **edges**.

40. Orientation of simplexes. A geometric m-simplex is uniquely determined by its vertices $P_0, P_1, \ldots, P_m$ and the order in which these points are taken is immaterial so far as the definition of § 39 is concerned. For certain purposes, however, it is necessary to take the order of the vertices into account. A **permutation** of σ^m is simply a permutation of its vertices. Thus there are $(m + 1)!$ possible permutations of σ^m. Two permutations are called equivalent if both are even or both are odd; otherwise they are called opposite. This determines an equivalence relation which separates the set of permutations of σ^m into two classes. These classes are called **orientations** of σ^m. A geometric m-simplex together with one or other of these two orientations is called an **oriented geometric m-simplex.** Thus every geometric m-simplex determines two oriented geometric m-simplexes.

For example, the two oriented 2-simplexes determined by three points P_0, P_1, P_2 can be represented by means of the diagrams in figure 21, in which the arrows indicate the orderings of the vertices.

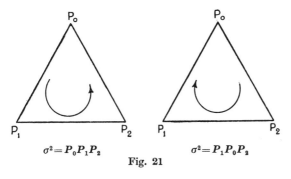

$$\sigma^2 = P_0 P_1 P_2 \qquad\qquad \sigma^2 = P_1 P_0 P_2$$

Fig. 21

To indicate the orientation we shall write $P_{\alpha_0} P_{\alpha_1} \ldots P_{\alpha_m}$ for an oriented geometric m-simplex; this will be taken to mean that the orientation is determined by the order $\alpha_0, \alpha_1, \ldots, \alpha_m$. Since there are only two distinct possibilities, and since $1, 0, 2, 3, \ldots, m$ is an odd permutation of $0, 1, 2, 3, \ldots, m$, any oriented geometric m-simplex determined by $m + 1$ vertices $P_0, P_1, \ldots, P_m$ can be written $P_0 P_1 P_2 \ldots P_m$ or $P_1 P_0 P_2 \ldots P_m$. We define $-P_0 P_1 P_2 \ldots P_m$ to be $P_1 P_0 P_2 \ldots P_m$. Thus, corresponding to a given set of $m + 1$ vertices we have two oriented geometric m-simplexes, $\sigma^m = P_0 P_1 \ldots P_m$ and $-\sigma^m$.

Henceforth we shall refer to an oriented open geometric m-simplex as an m-simplex; it will be understood that the word simplex means an open geometric simplex with one of the two possible orientations.

41. Simplicial Complexes.

A **geometrical simplicial complex** K (which will be referred to as a complex) is a finite set of disjoint m-simplexes $(m = 0, 1, \ldots, p)$ in n-dimensional Euclidean space such that, if $\sigma^m \epsilon K$, then all faces of σ^m are in K. The number p is called the **dimension** of K.

The point set union of all the simplexes in K, that is the set of all points which belong to some simplex in K, is called a **polyhedron** and is denoted by $|K|$. The complex K is called a covering complex of the polyhedron $|K|$. A complex must not be confused with a polyhedron, though both are defined in terms of the same set of points. A complex is a collection of simplexes, but a polyhedron is a set of points. Two different complexes can both be covering complexes of the same polyhedron.

Example. Figure 22 shows an example of a three-dimensional complex. The orientations of the 1- and 2- simplexes are indicated

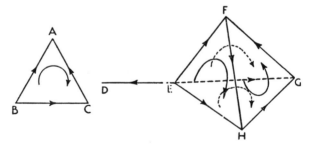

Fig. 22

by the arrows. They are chosen arbitrarily and are not necessarily related to one another. There is one 3-simplex, the tetrahedron $EFGH$. The 2-simplexes are the triangles BAC, EFH, FHG, EGH and EFG, of which all but the first are faces of $EFGH$. The 1-simplexes are BA, CA, BC, ED, EF, EH, EG, FH, GF, HG and the 0-simplexes are A, B, C, D, E, F, G, and H. The polyhedron covered by the complex in this case is not connected.

A **subcomplex** of a geometrical simplicial complex K is a subset of the simplexes of K which themselves form a complex. For example, in figure 22 the interior of the triangle BAC, the edges BC, CA, BA and the vertices A, B, C together form a subcomplex.

The **q-section** or **q-dimensional skeleton** of a complex K is the subcomplex consisting of all the simplexes σ^m of K for which $m \leq q$. Thus the 1-section of the complex in figure 22 consists of the edges BA, CA, BC, ED, EF, EH, EG, FH, GF, HG and the vertices A, B, C, D, E, F, G, H. It is obtained from the original complex by omitting the insides of the triangles and the tetrahedron.

A given m-simplex σ^m and all its faces form an m-dimensional complex, which is sometimes denoted by Cl σ^m. The corresponding polyhedron in this case is the closed m-simplex $\overline{\sigma}^m$.

A geometrical simplicial complex K consists of a finite set of simplexes, and, since the faces of each simplex are in K, the polyhedron $|K|$ can be regarded as the union of a finite number of closed simplexes. Hence $|K|$ is a closed and bounded subset of Euclidean space, and so, giving it the usual topology induced by the Euclidean space, it is a compact space.

42. Incidence. Let σ^m and τ^{m+1} be two oriented geometric simplexes in a complex **K**. The incidence number $[\tau^{m+1}; \sigma^m]$ of these two simplexes is defined as follows. If σ^m is not a face of τ^{m+1}, then $[\tau^{m+1}; \sigma^m] = 0$. If σ^m is a face of τ^{m+1}, and $\sigma^m = P_0 P_1 \ldots P_m$, then $\tau^{m+1} = \pm QP_0 P_1 \ldots P_m$ for some additional vertex Q; we put

$[\tau^{m+1};\ \sigma^m] = 1$ if $\tau^{m+1} = QP_0P_1\ldots P_m$ and $[\tau^{m+1};\ \sigma^m] = -1$ if $\tau^{m+1} = -QP_0P_1\ldots P_m$. When the incidence number of two simplexes is not zero, then we say that the two simplexes are **incident**.

Example. If $\tau^2 = ABC$ and $\sigma^1 = BA$, as in figure 23, then $\tau^2 = BCA = -CBA$, and so $[\tau^2;\ \sigma^1] = -1$. Notice that the two arrows in the diagram which indicate the orientation oppose one another; had they agreed, the incidence number would have been $+1$.

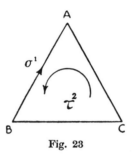

Fig. 23

If the m-simplexes of a given complex K are $\sigma_1^m,\ \ldots,\ \sigma_s^m$ and the $(m+1)$-simplexes are $\tau_1^{m+1},\ \ldots,\ \tau_r^{m+1}$, then we write η_{ij}^m for the incidence number $[\tau_i^{m+1};\ \sigma_j^m]$ $(i = 1,\ \ldots,\ r;\ j = 1,\ \ldots,\ s)$. The matrix of r rows and s columns which has η_{ij}^m as the element in the ith row and j^{th} column is called an **incidence matrix** and is denoted by I_m.

THEOREM 5.1 *The incidence matrices satisfy* $I_m I_{m-1} = 0$ $(m = 1,\ \ldots,\ p)$.

Proof. The number of columns of I_m is equal to the number of m-simplexes, and so it is equal to the number of rows of I_{m-1}. Hence the product $I_m I_{m-1}$ does exist. Let s be the number of m-simplexes. The element in the ith row and j^{th} column of $I_m I_{m-1}$ is $\sum_{k=1}^{s} \eta_{ik}^m \eta_{kj}^{m-1}$. If τ_i^{m+1} is not incident with σ_k^m, η_{ik}^m is zero, and if σ_k^m is not incident with the $(m-1)$-simplex ρ^{m-1}_j, η^{m-1}_{kj} is zero. Hence a given term in the sum $\sum\limits_{k=1}^{s} \eta^{m}_{ik} \eta^{m-1}_{kj}$ is zero unless σ^{m}_k is incident with both τ^{m+1}_i and ρ^{m-1}_j. If these conditions are satisfied, and if $\rho^{m-1}_j = Q_0 Q_1 \ldots Q_{m-1}$, then $\sigma^{m}_k = \eta^{m-1}_{kj} P \rho^{m-1}_j$ and $\tau^{m+1}_i = \eta^{m}_{ik} \eta^{m-1}_{kj} RP \rho^{m-1}_j$ where P is the additional vertex of σ^{m}_k and R is the additional vertex of τ^{m+1}_i. Therefore $\tau^{m+1}_i = -\eta^{m}_{ik} \eta^{m-1}_{kj} PR \rho^{m-1}_j = -\eta^{m-1}_{kj} P \sigma^{m}_h$, where σ^{m}_h is defined to be the m-simplex $\eta^{m}_{ik} R \rho^{m-1}_j$. Thus there exists an m-simplex, σ^{m}_h, incident with both τ^{m+1}_i and ρ^{m-1}_j, and such that the corresponding incidence numbers are $-\eta^{m-1}_{kj}$ and η^{m}_{ik}. Moreover $\pm\sigma^{m}_h$ is a simplex of the complex K, since all the faces of a given simplex in K are in K, and $\pm\sigma^{m}_h$ is a face of τ^{m+1}_i. Clearly σ^{m}_k and $\pm\sigma^{m}_h$ are the only two simplexes in K incident with both τ^{m+1}_i and ρ^{m-1}_j. Therefore to every non-zero term in $\sum\limits_{k=1}^{s} \eta^{m}_{ik} \eta^{m-1}_{kj}$, there corresponds another non-zero term equal in magnitude but opposite in sign. The value of the sum is therefore zero, and so $I_m I_{m-1} = 0$.

43. Triangulation. Given a geometric simplicial complex K, the associated polyhedron $|K|$ is uniquely defined; as we have seen, it is a compact subset of Euclidean space. Starting with a given polyhedron, the complex K is not uniquely determined; indeed infinitely many covering complexes can be constructed except in the trivial case when $|K|$ has just one point. The process of constructing a geometric simplicial complex which covers a polyhedron is known as **triangulation** of the polyhedron.

The idea of triangulation can be extended by allowing simplexes to be replaced by topologically equivalent sets. For example, compact surfaces in Euclidean space of three dimensions can be triangulated by means of points, curves and curvilinear triangles. Clearly if a compact subset S of

G

a Euclidean space is homeomorphic to a polyhedron P, then S can be triangulated by replacing the simplexes of a covering complex of P by their images under a fixed homeomorphism $f : P \to S$.

The most important reason for triangulating a space is to obtain topological invariants. In Chapter VI, we define the *homology groups* of simplicial complexes, and various associated numbers such as the *Euler characteristic*, the *Betti numbers* and the *torsion coefficients*. All these are topological invariants of the polyhedra associated with the simplicial complexes. This means that, if two complexes K, L are such that the polyhedra $|K|$ and $|L|$ are homeomorphic, then the corresponding homology groups are isomorphic and the corresponding associated numbers are equal. In particular, two covering complexes of a given polyhedron have isomorphic homology groups and the same associated numbers.

Three main features regarding such topological invariants are to be observed. First, they are defined in terms of triangulations; for example, in the case of two-dimensional surfaces the Euler characteristic is $F - E + V$, where F, E, and V are the numbers of faces, edges and vertices of a triangulation. Secondly, they are essentially independent of the method of triangulation, so that they are invariants, with respect to triangulations, of the polyhedra. Thirdly, this invariance is topological.

In Chapter VI, we are concerned solely with the first of these three features. No attempt is made to prove that homology groups are topological invariants. Nor do we discuss the restrictions which must be imposed on a space in order that it can be triangulated. These problems are too complicated to be discussed in a book of this nature. The reader is recommended to consult more advanced treatises after reading Chapter VI. A proof of the invariance of the homology groups is given in L. Pontrjagin's *Foundations of Combinatorial Topology*.

44. Examples of Triangulation.

Example 1. The eight curvilinear triangles *ABE*, *AED*, *ADF*, *AFB*, *BCE*, *CED*, *DCF*, *BFC* determine a triangulation of the sphere, as shown in figure 24. Each triangle and edge must be given one of the two possible orientations.

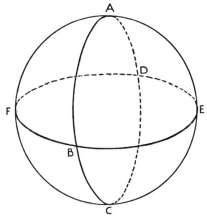

Fig. 24

Example 2. For the torus, the representation by means of a rectangle with opposite sides identified can be used. A triangulation is given in figure 25. This triangulation, which consists of 7 vertices, 21 edges

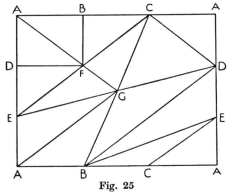

Fig. 25

and 14 triangles, is one which involves the least possible number of simplexes of each dimension. We observe that, if F is the number of faces, E the number of edges and V the number of vertices, then $F - E + V = 0$.

Example 3. For the real projective plane, we can use the representation given in figure 10. A possible triangulation, complete with orientations, is given in figure 26.

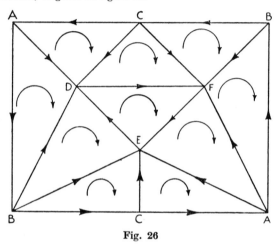

Fig. 26

The 0-simplexes are A, B, C, D, E, F. The 1-simplexes are

$a = BC$	$f = ED$	$k = AE$
$b = CA$	$g = CD$	$l = CE$
$c = AB$	$h = CF$	$m = BE$
$d = FE$	$i = BF$	$n = BD$
$e = DF$	$j = AF$	$o = AD$

and the 2-simplexes are

$\alpha = DFE$	$\zeta = FAE$
$\beta = ACD$	$\eta = EAC$
$\gamma = CFD$	$\theta = BEC$
$\delta = BFC$	$\iota = BDE$
$\varepsilon = BAF$	$\varkappa = ADB.$

The incidence matrices I_0 and I_1 are given by the following tables.

The appropriate simplexes have been written at the beginning of each row and column for convenience.

		A	B	C	D	E	F
	a	.	−1	1	.	.	.
	b	1	.	−1	.	.	.
	c	−1	1	.	.	.	.
	d	.	.	.	.	1	−1
	e	.	.	.	−1	.	1
	f	.	.	.	1	−1	.
	g	.	.	−1	1	.	.
I_0	h	.	.	−1	.	.	1
	i	.	−1	.	.	.	1
	j	−1	.	.	.	.	1
	k	−1	.	.	.	1	.
	l	.	.	−1	.	1	.
	m	.	−1	.	.	1	.
	n	.	−1	.	1	.	.
	o	−1	.	.	1	.	.

		a	b	c	d	e	f	g	h	i	j	k	l	m	n	o
	α	.	.	.	1	1	1	.	.	.	.	.	.	.	.	.
	β	.	−1	.	.	.	.	1	.	.	.	.	.	.	.	−1
	γ	.	.	.	.	−1	.	−1	1	.	.	.	.	.	.	.
	δ	−1	.	.	.	.	.	.	−1	1	.	.	.	.	.	.
I_1	ε	.	.	−1	.	.	.	.	.	−1	1	.	.	.	.	.
	ζ	.	.	.	−1	.	.	.	.	.	−1	1	.	.	.	.
	η	.	−1	.	.	.	.	.	.	.	.	−1	1	.	.	.
	θ	−1	.	.	.	.	.	.	.	.	.	.	−1	1	.	.
	ι	.	.	.	.	.	−1	.	.	.	.	.	.	−1	1	.
	κ	.	.	−1	.	.	.	.	.	.	.	.	.	.	−1	1

This example has been given in some detail, because it will be quoted from time to time in Chapter VI.

Exercises.

(1). Construct a triangulation of the Klein bottle, using the representation given in figure 9. Write down the incidence matrices I_0 and I_1.

(2). Prove that the triangulation of the real projective plane, given in figure 26, is one which involves the least possible numbers of simplexes of each dimension.

HOMOLOGY

45. Introduction. This chapter contains a brief introduction to the homology theory of simplicial complexes. It should be understood that this is only one of several homology theories. An exhaustive account is beyond the scope of this book.

The idea behind homology can conveniently be illustrated by the following description of the so-called 'mod 2' homology groups. Suppose that a surface is subdivided into regions, curves and vertices — for example, triangulated in the manner described in Chapter V. Consider any curve in the subdivision of the surface. It may have end-points which are vertices of the subdivision, but on the other hand it may be closed (in the sense of § 34) so that it has no end-points. In the latter case it is called a 1-*cycle*. Any given 1-cycle may or may not be the boundary of one of the regions into which the surface is subdivided. If a 1-cycle is the boundary of a region, it is called a *bounding* 1-*cycle*. Two 1-cycles are called *homologous* if together they form a bounding 1-cycle, that is if together they bound a region. This determines an equivalence relation in the set of all 1-cycles, which can therefore be separated into classes such that any two 1-cycles in a given class are homologous. These classes are called *homology classes*. Defining addition of homology classes in the natural way, we obtain a group, known as the 1-*dimensional homology group*. Homology groups in other dimensions can also be defined in a similar manner, and the ideas can be extended to a wider class of spaces than surfaces. To define homology groups in general, it is necessary to introduce the additional concept of orientation; in the 'mod 2' homology theory orientation is of no significance. The reason for this is given in § 52.

The significance of the homology groups lies in the fact that they are topological invariants. This means that homeomorphic spaces have isomorphic homology groups. In fact, the homology groups, like the homotopy groups, satisfy the stronger condition of being invariants of homotopy type (see Chapter IV). However, neither of these theorems will be proved in this book.

Homology resembles homotopy in many ways. For example, two 1-cycles on the torus are homologous if and only if they are homotopic. However, this property is not true for surfaces in general. Consider, for example, the surface obtained by removing the interior of a simply-connected region from the surface of a torus, as shown in figure 27, in which the region removed is shaded. On this

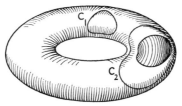

Fig. 27

surface, the curve bounding the shaded region is not homotopic to zero, because it cannot be contracted continuously over the surface into a point; but it is homologous to zero, because it is the boundary of the whole surface. Again, although the curves C_1 and C_2 shown in the figure are not homotopic, they are homologous.

46. Finitely generated Abelian groups. Some knowledge of the theory of Abelian groups, and particularly finitely generated Abelian groups, is required for the understanding of the substance of this chapter. It will be assumed that the reader is familiar with Chapter VI of W. Ledermann's book †, *Introduction to the Theory of Finite Groups*. However, we shall give a résumé of the definitions and results, including some theorems not proved in Ledermann's book. The reader who is not interested in the algebraic background can omit the proofs, but should at least be familiar with the results.

An additive Abelian group G is said to be **finitely generated** if there are elements $g_1, \ldots, g_s$ of G such that every element of G can be expressed in the form $u_1 g_1 + u_2 g_2 + \ldots + u_s g_s$ where $u_1, u_2, \ldots, u_s$ are integers. We shall require the following properties of such groups.

THEOREM A. *If G is a finitely generated Abelian group, and H is a subgroup of G, then H is a finitely generated Abelian group.*

Proof. Suppose that $s = 1$; then every element of G is of the form ug where u is an integer and g is some element of G. Let H be a subgroup of G. Then every element of H is also of the form ug. If $u = 0$ is the only possible value of u corresponding to elements of H, then H is the identity and the theorem is satisfied trivially. If there are elements $ug \in H$ such that $u \neq 0$, then there are elements $ug \in H$ such that u is positive, for if $ug \in H$ then $-ug \in H$ since H is a group. Let v be the least positive value of u for which $ug \in H$. Then, for any non-zero value u_0 of u such that $u_0 g \in H$, we can write $u_0 = qv + r$, where q and r are integers and $0 \leqq r < v$. Consider the elements $u_0 g$, vg of H. Since H is a group, $q(vg)$ is an element of H and so $u_0 g - qvg = (u_0 - qv)g = rg$ is an element of H. But the least positive value of u such that $ug \in H$ is v. Therefore $r = 0$. Hence $u_0 g = q(vg)$ and so any element of H is of the form $q(vg)$. Therefore H is finitely generated by the single element vg of H.

Thus we have proved that the theorem is true in the case $s = 1$. To prove that the theorem is true in general,

† We use the additive notation of the second edition. In the first edition, multiplicative notation was used.

we use induction. Suppose that the theorem is true for $s = m$. Let G be an Abelian group generated by $m + 1$ elements $g_1, \ldots, g_{m+1}$. Then the elements of the form $u_1 g_1 + u_2 g_2 + \ldots + u_m g_m$, where the u's are integers, form a subgroup G^* of G. The intersection H^* of H with G^* forms a subgroup of G^*. Since G^* is finitely generated, so is H^*, by the induction hypothesis.

Let $h = v_1 g_1 + \ldots + v_{m+1} g_{m+1}$ be an element of H. If v_{m+1} is zero for all elements of H, then H is contained in G^*, and so, by the induction hypothesis, it is finitely generated. If v_{m+1} is non-zero for some elements of H, then there are elements for which it is positive, for, since H is a group, $-h \, \epsilon \, H$ whenever $h \, \epsilon \, H$. Let h' be an element of H for which v_{m+1} attains its least possible positive value, and denote this value by v'_{m+1}. If $v_{m+1} \neq 0$, we can write $v_{m+1} = q v'_{m+1} + r$, where q and r are integers, and $0 \leqq r < v'_{m+1}$. Consider the element $h - qh' = (v_1 - q v'_1) g_1 + \ldots + (v_{m+1} - q v'_{m+1}) g_{m+1}$. This is in H, since h and h' are in H. But the coefficient of g_{m+1} is r, which is a non-negative integer less than v'_{m+1}. Therefore $r = 0$. Hence $h - qh'$ is an element of G^*, and so it belongs to H^*. But H^* is finitely generated, and so H is finitely generated by h' and the generators of H^*.

Therefore, if the theorem is true for $s = m$, it is true for $s = m + 1$. But it is true for $s = 1$. Hence, by induction, it is true for all values of s.

THEOREM B. *If G is a finitely generated Abelian group, and H is a subgroup of G, then the difference group $G - H$ is a finitely generated Abelian group.*

Proof. $G - H$ consists of classes of elements of G, two elements of G being in the same class if and only if their difference is in H (see Ledermann, loc. cit., p. 138). Addition of such classes is defined by

$$[g] + [g'] = [g + g']$$

where $g, g' \, \epsilon \, G$. It follows that, if $u_1, u_2, \ldots, u_s$ are integers, then

$$[u_1g_1 + \ldots + u_sg_s] = u_1[g_1] + \ldots + u_s[g_s]$$

for any elements $g_1, \ldots, g_s$ of G. Therefore, if G is generated by $g_1, \ldots, g_s$, then $G - H$ is generated by $[g_1], \ldots, [g_s]$.

THEOREM C (BASIS THEOREM). *If G is a finitely generated Abelian group there exist elements $e_1, \ldots, e_q$ of orders $m_1, \ldots, m_q$ respectively, (so that m_i is the least non-zero positive integer for which $m_ie_i = 0$) such that m_i divides m_{i-1} ($i = 2, 3, \ldots, q$), and elements $f_1, \ldots, f_r$ of infinite order such that G can be expressed as a direct sum of the form*

$$G = \{e_1\} \oplus \{e_2\} \oplus \ldots \oplus \{e_q\} \oplus \{f_1\} \oplus \ldots \oplus \{f_r\},$$

where $\{e_i\}$ is the cyclic group of order m_i generated by e_i, and $\{f_i\}$ is the infinite cyclic group generated by f_i. The numbers $m_1, \ldots, m_q$ and r are uniquely determined by G.

This is the fundamental theorem on finitely generated Abelian groups. A proof can be found in Ledermann's book on page 155. The numbers $m_1, \ldots, m_q$ are called the **torsion coefficients** of G, and r is called the **rank** of G.

THEOREM D. *If H is a subgroup of a finitely generated Abelian group, then the rank of G is equal to the sum of the ranks of H and $G - H$.*

Proof. A set of elements $g_1, \ldots, g_s$ of an Abelian group is is said to be linearly independent if $u_1g_1 + u_2g_2 + \ldots + u_sg_s = 0$, where the u's are integers, implies that $u_i = 0$ ($i = 1, \ldots, s$). We shall show that the rank of a finitely generated Abelian group is equal to the maximum number of linearly independent elements. Let f_i ($i = 1, \ldots, r$) be as in the above statement of the Basis Theorem. Then the f's are linearly independent, for if $u_1f_1 + \ldots + u_rf_r = 0$, then $u_if_i = 0$ ($i = 1, \ldots, r$), since G is the direct sum of $\{e_1\}, \ldots, \{e_q\}, \{f_1\}, \ldots, \{f_r\}$; but $u_if_i = 0$ implies that $u_i = 0$, since f_i is of infinite order. Therefore there are at least r linearly independent elements of G. Now let g be any element of G. Then we can write

$$g = v_1e_1 + \ldots + v_qe_q + w_1f_1 + \ldots + w_rf_r$$

for some integers $v_1, \ldots, v_q$, $w_1, \ldots, w_r$. Hence

$$m_q g = m_q w_1 f_1 + \ldots + m_q w_r f_r$$

since the element e_i is of order m_i, and m_i is divisible by m_{i-1}. Therefore the elements g, $f_1, \ldots, f_r$ are linearly dependent, and it follows quickly that every set of $r + 1$ elements is linearly dependent. Hence the maximum number of linearly independent elements of G is the rank of G.

Let r, s, t be the ranks of G, H, and $G - H$ respectively. Let $h_1, \ldots, h_s$ be a system of linearly independent elements of H, and $k_1, \ldots, k_t$ a system of linearly independent elements of $G - H$. Then each element k_i is a class of elements of G; let g_i be a representative of the class of k_i, so that g_i is an element of G such that $k_i = [g_i]$. If

$$u_1 g_1 + \ldots + u_t g_t + v_1 h_1 + \ldots + v_s h_s = 0$$

where the u's and the v's are integers, then

$$u_1 [g_1] + \ldots + u_t [g_t] + v_1 [h_1] + \ldots + v_s [h_s] = 0$$

by the property mentioned in the proof of Theorem B. But the class of any element of H is the zero class, and so

$$u_1 k_1 + \ldots + u_t k_t = 0.$$

Hence, since the k's are linearly independent, $u_i = 0$ $(i = 1, \ldots, t)$. Therefore $v_1 h_1 + \ldots + v_s h_s = 0$; but the h's are linearly independent, and therefore $v_i = 0$ $(i = 1, \ldots, s)$. It follows that $g_1, \ldots, g_t, h_1, \ldots, h_s$ are linearly independent elements of G, and so $r \geqq s + t$.

Let g be any element of G, and k the corresponding class of elements of G in $G - H$. Then $uk + u_1 k_1 + \ldots + u_t k_t = 0$ for some integers $u, u_1, \ldots, u_t$ not all zero. Since $k_1, \ldots, k_t$ are linearly independent, $u \neq 0$. Consider the element $h = ug + u_1 g_1 + \ldots + u_t g_t$ of G. Since the class of this element in $G - H$ is $uk + u_1 k_1 + \ldots + u_t k_t$, which is zero by hypothesis, it follows that $h \in H$. Hence $vh + v_1 h_1 + \ldots + v_s h_s = 0$ for some integers $v, v_1, \ldots, v_s$ not all zero;

and since $h_1, \ldots, h_s$ are linearly independent, v is non-zero. Hence

$$uvg + u_1 v g_1 + \ldots + u_t v g_t + v_1 h_1 + \ldots + v_s h_s = 0,$$

and the coefficient of g, being uv, is non-zero. Thus every set of $s + t + 1$ elements of G is linearly dependent, and so $r \leqq s + t$. Combining this with the previous result, we see that $r = s + t$.

In addition to the above properties of finitely generated Abelian groups, we shall require the following theorem.

THEOREM E. *Let G be any additive group. Then a subset $H \subset G$ is a subgroup of G if and only if $a \in H$ and $b \in H$ imply that $a - b \in H$.*

Proof. If H satisfies the given condition, then (i) $0 \in H$ since $a - a = 0$, (ii) $a \in H$ implies that $-a \in H$, for $0 \in H$ by (i) and so $0 - a = -a \in H$, (iii) $a, b \in H$ imply that $a, -b \in H$ by (ii) and so $a + b = a - (-b) \in H$ and (iv) the associative law is satisfied in H because G is a group and the elements of H are in G.

Conversely, if H is a subgroup of G, then $a, b \in H$ imply that $a, -b \in H$ and so $a - b \in H$.

47. Chains. Let K be an n-dimensional geometric simplicial complex, and let α_p $(p = 0, 1, \ldots, n)$ be the number of p-simplexes in K. An **integral p-chain** c^p is a set of α_p integers $u_1, u_2, \ldots, u_{\alpha_p}$ associated respectively with the p-simplexes $\sigma_1^p, \sigma_2^p, \ldots, \sigma_{\alpha_p}^p$ of K. Symbolically we write

$$c^p = u_1 \sigma_1^p + u_2 \sigma_2^p + \ldots + u_{\alpha_p} \sigma_{\alpha_p}^p = \sum_{i=1}^{\alpha_p} u_i \sigma_i^p$$

and regard c^p as a linear form over the p-simplexes of K, with integral coefficients. We also write $(-1)\sigma^p$ for the simplex $-\sigma^p$.

If $c_1^p = \sum u_i \sigma_i^p$ and $c_2^p = \sum v_i \sigma_i^p$ are two integral p-chains, we define their sum $c_1^p + c_2^p$ to be the integral p-chain

$\Sigma(u_i + v_i)\sigma_i^p$. With respect to addition defined in this way, the set of all p-chains of K forms an Abelian group C^p. For the sum of two p-chains is a p-chain, the associative law is satisfied because addition of integers is associative, the p-chain for which all the coefficients are zero (the zero p-chain) is the identity and the inverse of $\Sigma u_i\sigma_i^p$ is $\Sigma(-u_i)\sigma_i^p$.

Example. Referring to the complex of figure 26, $A + C + 2E$ is an integral 0-chain, $2a - 3c - f$ is an integral 1-chain. It would be more accurate to write $1A + 0B + 1C + 0D + 2E + 0F$ for the chain $A + C + 2E$. However, it is convenient to write σ^p instead of $1\sigma^p$, and to omit the terms whose coefficients are zero. It is also convenient to write 0 for the zero p-chain irrespective of the value of p. The zero p-chain is in fact often referred to as 'zero'.

48. Boundaries. The **boundary** of a p-simplex σ_i^p $(p > 0)$ in a complex K is the integral $(p-1)$-chain $\varDelta\sigma_i^p = \Sigma\eta_{ij}^{p-1}\tau_j^{p-1}$, where η_{ij}^{p-1} is the incidence number between σ_i^p and τ_j^{p-1}. The boundary of a 0-simplex is defined to be zero. The definition of boundary is extended to chains as follows. The boundary $\varDelta c^p$ $(p > 0)$ of the integral p-chain $c^p = \Sigma u_i\sigma_i^p$ is the integral $(p-1)$-chain $\Sigma_i u_i\varDelta\sigma_i^p = \Sigma_{i,j} u_i\eta_{ij}^{p-1}\tau_j^{p-1}$; the boundary of a 0-chain is zero. The fundamental property of boundaries is expressed by the following theorem.

THEOREM 6.1 *The boundary of the boundary of a p-chain is zero (symbolically $\varDelta\varDelta c^p = 0$).*

Proof. If $p > 0$, $\varDelta c^p = \varDelta\Sigma u_i\sigma_i^p$ is the chain $\Sigma u_i\eta_{ij}^{p-1}\tau_j^{p-1}$. The boundary of this is zero if $p = 1$, and if $p > 1$ it is the integral $(p-2)$-chain $\Sigma_{i,j,k} u_i\eta_{ij}^{p-1}\eta_{jk}^{p-2}\omega_k^{p-2}$, where the ω_k^{p-2} are the $(p-2)$-simplexes. But, by Theorem 5.1, $\Sigma\eta_{ij}^{p-1}\eta_{jk}^{p-2} = 0$. Hence $\varDelta(\varDelta c^p) = 0$.

Example. In the complex of figure 26, the boundary of the integral 2-chain $\alpha + 2\beta + 3\delta + \theta$ is $(d + e + f) + 2(-b + g - o) + 3(-a - h + i) + (-a - l + m) = -4a - 2b + d + e + f + 2g - 3h - l + m + 3i - 2o$. The boundaries of the individual 2-simplexes are readily obtained from the incidence matrix I_1. For example, the boundary of α is obtained by adding together the appropriate 1-simplexes corresponding to the non-zero elements in the row opposite α.

If c_1^p and c_2^p are two p-chains, then $\Delta(c_1^p + c_2^p) = \Delta c_1^p + \Delta c_2^p$. Thus Δ is a homomorphism of C^p into C^{p-1}.

49. Cycles.

An **integral p-cycle** over K is an integral p-chain whose boundary is zero. The set of all p-cycles forms a subgroup Z^p of C^p. For if c_1^p and c_1^p are two p-cycles, then $\Delta c_1^p = 0 = \Delta c_2^p$. Hence $\Delta(c_1^p - c_2^p) = \Delta c_1^p - \Delta c_2^p = 0$, so that $c_1^p - c_2^p$ is also a p-cycle. Therefore, by Theorem E the set of all p-cycles forms a subgroup of C^p.

An immediate consequence of Theorem 6.1 is that the boundary of a $(p + 1)$-chain is a p-cycle. For, if $c^p = \Delta c^{p+1}$, then $\Delta c^p = \Delta(\Delta c^{p+1}) = 0$. However a p-cycle is not necessarily the boundary of a $(p + 1)$-chain.

Example 1. In the complex of figure 26, $\Delta\alpha = d + e + f$. Therefore $d + e + f$ is a 1-cycle which is the boundary of a 2-simplex. That $d + e + f$ is a 1-cycle can easily be verified; $\Delta(d + e + f) = (E - F) + (-D + F) + (D - E) = 0$.

Example 2. In the same complex, $a + b + c$ is a 1-cycle. For $\Delta(a + b + c) = (-B + C) + (A - C) + (-A + B) = 0$. But $a + b + c$ is not the boundary of an integral 2-cycle. For if it were, we should have

$$a + b + c = \Delta(v_1\alpha + v_2\beta + \ldots + v_{10}\varkappa)$$
$$= v_1(d + e + f) + v_2(-b + g - o) + v_3(-e - g + h)$$
$$+ v_4(-a - h + i) + v_5(-c - i + j) + v_6(-d - j + k)$$
$$+ v_7(-b - k + l) + v_8(-a - l + m) + v_9(-f - m + n)$$
$$+ v_{10}(-c - n + o),$$

for some integers $v_1, v_2, \ldots, v_{10}$. By considering the coefficients of $d, e, f, g, \ldots, o$, we see that all the v's are equal. Then $a + b + c = -2v_1(a + b + c)$. But this implies that $2v_1 = -1$, which is impossible since v_1 is an integer.

Example 3. In the same complex, there are no non-zero integral 2-cycles. For, by the same process as used in example 2, $\Delta(v_1\alpha + v_2\beta + \ldots + v_{10}\varkappa) = 0$ implies that all the v's are zero. Thus, in this case, the group Z^2 consists of a single element, the zero 2-chain.

An integral p-cycle of the form Δc^{p+1}, where c^{p+1} is a $(p+1)$-chain, is called a **bounding p-cycle.** The set of all bounding p-cycles in a given complex K is a subgroup B^p of Z^p. For, if $c_1^p = \Delta c^{p+1}_1$ and $c_2^p = \Delta c^{p+1}_2$, then $c_1^p - c_2^p = \Delta c^{p+1}_1 - \Delta c^{p+1}_2 = \Delta(c^{p+1}_1 - c^{p+1}_2)$, and therefore $c_1^p - c_2^p$ is a bounding p-cycle. The fact that B^p is a subgroup of Z^p then follows from Theorem E.

Thus, associated with any geometric simplicial complex K, we have three sets of groups C^p, Z^p, B^p, which satisfy the inclusion relationships $B^p \subset Z^p \subset C^p$. The operator Δ is, in fact, a homomorphism of C^p onto B^{p-1} such that the image of Z^p is zero.

50. Homology Groups. Let c_1^p and c_2^p be two integral p-chains. If $c_1^p - c_2^p$ is a bounding p-cycle, we write $c_1^p \sim c_2^p$ and say that c_1^p is **homologous** to c_2^p. In particular, if c^p is a bounding p-cycle, then $c^p \sim 0$ and we say that c^p is homologous to zero.

The relation $\sim$ is an equivalence relation†. For (i) it is reflexive, since $c^p - c^p = 0$, so that any cycle is homologous to itself; (ii) it is symmetric, since $c_1^p - c_2^p = \Delta c^{p+1}$ implies that $c_2^p - c_1^p = \Delta(-c^{p+1})$; (iii) it is transitive, since if $c_1^p - c_2^p = \Delta c^{p+1}_1$ and $c_2^p - c_3^p = \Delta c^{p+1}_2$, then $c_1^p - c_3^p = \Delta(c^{p+1}_1 + c^{p+1}_2)$. Thus the relation separates the set of all integral p-chains into mutually exclusive classes, called integral homology classes of dimension p; in particular it separates the set of all integral p-cycles into mutually

---

† The reader should distinguish carefully between the symbols $\sim$ here defined and $\smile$ as defined on p. 71.

exclusive classes. If $[c_1^p]$ and $[c_2^p]$ are two such classes of p-cycles, we define their sum by

$$[c_1^p] + [c_2^p] = [c_1^p + c_2^p].$$

It is easily shown that this defines the sum uniquely, for it is independent of the representatives of the classes. If $[0]$ denotes the class of bounding cycles, then

$$[c^p] + [0] = [c^p],$$
$$[c^p] + [-c^p] = [0].$$

Furthermore, addition defined in this way is associative, since addition of p-cycles is associative. Therefore the set of homology classes of dimension p forms an Abelian group H^p, called the pth **integral homology group** of K. It is of course just the difference group † $Z^p - B^p$.

The significance of the difference group $C^p - Z^p$ is shown by the next theorem.

THEOREM 6.2. *The difference group* $C^p - Z^p$ *is isomorphic with* B^{p-1} $(p = 1, 2, \ldots)$.

Proof. To each p-chain c^p $(p > 0)$ there corresponds a unique $(p-1)$-chain Δc^p; two p-chains c_1^p, c_2^p correspond to the same $(p-1)$-chain if and only if $\Delta(c_1^p - c_2^p) = 0$, that is, if and only if $c_1^p - c_2^p$ is a p-cycle. The elements of $C^p - Z^p$ are classes of p-chains, two chains being in the same class if and only if their difference is a p-cycle. If $[c^p]$ denotes such a class, then a one-one transformation $f : C^p - Z^p \to B^{p-1}$ is uniquely defined by $f[c^p] = \Delta c^p$. Moreover,

$$f([c_1^p] + [c_2^p]) = \Delta(c_1^p + c_2^p) = \Delta c_1^p + \Delta c_2^p = f[c_1^p] + f[c_2^p]$$

and so f is an isomorphism.

---

† See Ledermann, loc. cit., p. 138. The group $Z^p - B^p$ is sometimes called the factor group of Z^p with respect to B^p, and is denoted by Z^p/B^p. However it seems more reasonable to reserve this notation for multiplicative groups, and to use additive notation consistently for Abelian groups.

A complex K is said to be **connected** if it is not the union of two non-empty subcomplexes which have no simplexes in common; K is connected if and only if $|K|$ is connected. We shall show that the 0-dimensional integral homology group is isomorphic with the additive group of integers for a connected complex. To prove this, we first require the following theorem.

THEOREM 6.3 *A necessary and sufficient condition for a complex K to be connected is that, for every pair of vertices P, Q there is a sequence of vertices $P_1(=P)$, P_2, ..., $P_r(=Q)$ such that P_i and P_{i+1} are the vertices of a 1-simplex of K.*

Proof. Let K be a connected complex. If P is any vertex of K, and K_0 is the set of all vertices of K which can be joined to P by a sequence of the form stated in the theorem, then the set of all simplexes of K which have vertices in K_0 forms a subcomplex L. The set of all simplexes which are not in L, if there are any, forms a second subcomplex M which does not intersect L. But K is connected, and so M is empty. Hence all pairs of vertices can be joined in the manner described.

Conversely, suppose that all pairs of vertices can be joined in this way. If K is not connected, it is the union of two disjoint non-empty subcomplexes L and M. Let P be a vertex of L, and Q a vertex of M. Consider a sequence P_1, P_2, P_3, ..., P_{r-1}, P_r which connects P to Q. Let P_i be the first member of this sequence which is in M. Then $i > 1$, and so P_{i-1} exists and is in L; therefore $P_{i-1}P_i$ cannot be a simplex of K. Thus the hypothesis that K is not connected is false.

THEOREM 6.4 *If K is a connected complex, the integral homology group H^0 is isomorphic with the additive group of integers.*

Proof. Let P and Q be any two vertices of K. Then there is a sequence $P_1 (=P)$, P_2, ..., P_{r-1}, $P_r (=Q)$ of vertices of K such that P_i, P_{i+1} are the vertices of a 1-simplex. Let σ_i^1 be the 1-simplex $P_{i+1}P_i$. Then $\varDelta\sigma_i^1 = P_i - P_{i+1}$.

Hence $\varDelta \sum\limits_{i=1}^{r-1} u \, \sigma_i^1 = uP - uQ$, where u is any integer.
Therefore uP is homologous to uQ, and so, if $\sum u_i\sigma_i^0$ is
any 0-cycle, it is homologous to the 0-cycle $(\sum u_i)P$. Thus
every 0-cycle of K is homologous to one of the form uP,
where u is an integer. Two distinct 0-cycles uP, vP of this
form are not homologous, for if they were $(u - v)P$ would
be a bounding 0-cycle, which is impossible since $u \neq v$.
Therefore there is a one-one correspondence between the
homology classes of 0-cycles of K and the set of integers.
Under this correspondence, if u and v correspond to two
homology classes, then $u + v$ corresponds to their sum.
Hence H^0 is isomorphic with the additive group of integers.

Example. For the complex of figure 26, H^0 is isomorphic with
the additive group of integers, because of Theorem 6.4 and the fact
that the complex is connected. We now determine H^1 and H^2 by
direct methods.

H^1. Let $c^1 = \sum\limits_i u_i\sigma_i^1$ be an integral 1-cycle. Then $\varDelta c^1 = 0$, and so
$\sum\limits_i u_i\eta_{ij}^0 = 0$ $(j = 1, \ldots, 6)$. If c^1 is a bounding 1-cycle, then $c^1 = \varDelta c^2$
for some 2-chain $c^2 = \sum\limits_h v_h\tau_h$ say. Hence $\sum\limits_h u_h\sigma_h^1 = \sum\limits_{h,i} v_h\eta_{hi}^1\sigma_i^1$. Equating
coefficients, we obtain the following fifteen equations in the unknowns
$v_1, \ldots, v_{10}$.

$$\sum\limits_h v_h\eta_{hi}^1 = u_i \quad (i = 1, \ldots, 15; \ h = 1, \ldots, 10).$$

An examination of these equations together with the previous six
shows that they are consistent if and only if the equation

$$- 2v_{10} = u_3 + u_{10} + u_{11} + u_{12} + u_{13} + u_{14}$$

has a solution for v_{10}. This is so if and only if the right-hand side
is even. It follows that there are exactly two distinct homology classes
of dimension one. One of these corresponds to bounding 1-cycles,
and the other to non-bounding cycles c^1 such that $2c^1$ is a bounding
cycle. Hence H^1 is a cyclic group of order two.

H^2. If $c^2 = \sum\limits_i u_i\sigma_i^2$ is a 2-cycle, then we find, after some calculation,
that all the u's are equal, and that $2u_1 = 0$. Hence, since the u's

are integers, the only 2-cycle is the zero 2-cycle. Therefore H^2 is just the identity.

51. Betti numbers. Any integral p-chain over a complex K is expressible as a finite sum, with integral coefficients, of a basic set of p-chains, the p-simplexes $\sigma_1^p, \ldots, \sigma_{\alpha_p}^p$. Therefore the group C^p is a finitely generated Abelian group, and so, by Theorems A and B of § 46, Z^p, B^p and $H^p = Z^p - B^p$ are also finitely generated Abelian groups. Thus the pth homology group H^p satisfies the conditions of Theorem C; its rank is called the pth **Betti number** b_p of K, and the torsion coefficients $m_1, \ldots, m_q$ are called the p-**dimensional torsion coefficients** of K. The direct sum of the finite cyclic groups occurring in the decomposition of H^p given by Theorem C is called the pth **torsion group** and the direct sum of the infinite cyclic groups is called the pth **Betti group**, though this term is sometimes taken to mean what we have called the pth homology group.

The following theorem shows how the Betti numbers can be calculated from the incidence matrices.

THEOREM 6.5. *If α_p is the number of p-simplexes of a complex K of dimension n, and r_p is the rank† of the incidence matrix I_p, then the pth Betti number b_p is given by*
$$b_p = \alpha_p - r_p - r_{p-1} \quad (p = 1, 2, \ldots)$$
$$b_0 = \alpha_0 - r_0.$$
Proof. The group C^p consists of all possible linear combinations with integral coefficients, of the simplexes $\sigma_1^p, \ldots, \sigma_{\alpha_p}^p$. Hence its rank is α_p. The group B^p consists of all p-chains of the form Δc^{p+1}, where c^{p+1} is a $(p+1)$-chain. Hence every element of B^p is of the form $\sum_{i,j} u_i \eta_{ij}^p \sigma_j^p$, so that B^p is generated by the elements $\sum \eta_{ij}^p \sigma_j^p$. Its rank is therefore the rank r_p of the matrix I_p. The pth Betti

† The matrices I_p exist only for $p = 0, 1, \ldots, n - 1$. However, we define r_p to be zero for $p \geq n$.

number b_p is, by definition, the rank of $Z^p - B^p$. But, by Theorem D of § 46, the rank of Z^p is equal to the sum of the ranks of B^p and $Z^p - B^p$, that is to $r_p + b_p$. If $0 < p < n$, $C^p - Z^p$ is isomorphic with B^{p-1}, by Theorem 6.2. Therefore, again using Theorem D of § 46, the rank of C^p is equal to the rank of Z^p plus the rank of B^{p-1}. Hence the rank of Z^p is equal to $\alpha_p - r_{p-1}$, and so $\alpha_p - r_{p-1} = b_p + r_p$. If $p = 0$, $C^p = Z^p$, and so $b_0 = \alpha_0 - r_0$. If $p = n$, there are no bounding p-cycles since there are no $(p + 1)$-chains. Hence b_n is equal to the rank of Z^n, which is $\alpha_n - r_n - r_{n-1}$, since $r_n = 0$. If $p > n$, the formula is trivial, since b_p, α_p, r_p and r_{p-1} are all zero.

Example. In the complex of figure 26, $\alpha_0 = 6$, $\alpha_1 = 15$, $\alpha_2 = 10$, $r_0 = 5$ and $r_1 = 10$. Hence $b_0 = 1$, $b_1 = 0$, $b_2 = 0$.

Elimination of $r_0, r_1, \ldots$ from the above relationships shows that the expressions $\sum_p (-1)^p b_p$ and $\sum_p (-1)^p \alpha_p$ have the same value. This is called the **Euler characteristic** of K. It is denoted by $\chi(K)$. For the complex of figure 26, $\chi(K) = 1$. For surfaces of two dimensions, the Euler characteristic is $F - E + V$, where F, E and V are the numbers of faces, edges and vertices respectively of a triangulation, since $\alpha_0 = V$, $\alpha_1 = E$ and $\alpha_2 = F$.

52. Chains over an arbitrary Abelian group.
Integral chains were defined in § 47. Many of their properties are retained if the coefficients are replaced by elements of a more general nature than integers. If G is any Abelian group, written additively, then a **p-chain over G** is a set of α_p elements $g_1, \ldots, g_{\alpha_p}$ of G associated respectively with the p-simplexes of K. Such a p-chain is conveniently represented by

$$c^p = g_1 \sigma_1^p + g_2 \sigma_2^p + \ldots + g_{\alpha_p} \sigma_{\alpha_p}^p.$$

Addition of p-chains over G is defined in the natural way, as for integral p-chains. With respect to addition, the set of all p-chains over G forms an Abelian group $C^p(K, G)$.

If G is the additive group of rational numbers, then a p-chain over G is called a rational p-chain. Similarly, we speak of real p-chains and p-chains modulo a prime number π; in these cases G is the additive group of real numbers and the additive group of integers mod π respectively. If $\pi = 2$, $-\sigma^p = \sigma^p$. Thus orientation of simplexes need not be taken into account when considering p-chains mod 2.

The boundary of a p-chain over G is defined in the same way as for integral p-chains. The boundary of a p-simplex σ_i^p is first defined to be the integral $(p-1)$-chain $\Sigma \eta_{ij}^{p-1} \tau_j^{p-1}$. Then the boundary of the p-chain $\Sigma g_i \sigma_i^p$ is defined to be the $(p-1)$-chain $\Sigma_{i,j} g_i \eta_{ij}^{p-1} \tau_j^{p-1}$ over G. Here $g_i 1$ and $g_i(-1)$ are to be interpreted as g_i and $-g_i$ in the usual way.

For any group G, the boundary of the boundary of a p-chain is zero. A p-cycle over G is a p-chain over G whose boundary is zero, and a bounding p-cycle over G is a p-chain over G of the form Δc^{p+1}. The set of all p-cycles forms a subgroup $Z^p(K, G)$ of $C^p(K, G)$, and the set of bounding p-cycles a subgroup $B^p(K, G)$ of $Z^p(K, G)$. The difference group $Z^p(K, G) - B^p(K, G)$ is called the pth homology group of K over G, and is denoted by $H^p(K, G)$.

Theorems 6.2 and 6.4 are readily generalised to the case of an arbitrary Abelian group. The proof of Theorem 6.2 goes over without modification, and the generalisation of Theorem 6.4 states that, for a connected complex, $H^0(K, G)$ is isomorphic with G.

Example. Returning again to the complex of figure 26, we can calculate the homology groups in the same way as we did when G was the group of integers. It must be remembered, however, that the elements of G need not satisfy all the properties of integers which were used previously.

H^1. Here the analysis depends on whether the equation

$$- 2v_{10} = u_3 + u_{10} + u_{11} + u_{12} + u_{13} + u_{14}$$

has a solution for v_{10}. If G is the additive group of rational numbers, the equation always has a solution for v_{10}. In this case, therefore, every 1-cycle is a bounding 1-cycle, and so H^1 consists of the identity element alone.

H^2. In the previous case when G was the group of integers, it was shown that H^2 reduces to the identity. This depended at one stage on the fact that there is no non-zero integer u such that $u + u = 0$. However, an Abelian group may contain elements of order two, that is elements g such that $g+g = 0$. For example, every element of the additive group of integers mod 2 (which consists of two elements, the class of odd integers and the class of even integers) satisfies this condition. In this case there is a single non-zero 2-cycle, namely $\sum_i \sigma_i^2$. This cycle is not a bounding 2-cycle, since K contains no 3-simplexes. Thus there are exactly two distinct homology classes, each of which consists of a single cycle. The group $H^2(K, G)$ is then a cyclic group of order two.

A set of p-chains $c_1^p, \ldots, c_s^p$ over G is said to be **linearly independent with respect to homology** if there are no elements $g_1, \ldots, g_s$ of G, not all zero, such that $\sum_i g_i c_i^p$ is a bounding p-cycle over G. The maximum number of p-cycles over G linearly independent with respect to homology is sometimes called the pth **Betti number** of K with respect to G and is denoted by $b_p(K, G)$. When G is the group of integers, it is the pth Betti number as defined in § 51.

It can be shown that, if G is the additive group of integers modulo a prime number π, then the result of Theorem 6.5 is still true. Thus the Betti numbers mod π can be calculated from the ranks mod π of the incidence matrices.

Referring again to the complex of figure 26, the rank of the incidence matrix I_1 is 10 unless $\pi = 2$, in which case it is 9. It follows that $b_1(K, G)$ and $b_2(K, G)$ are both zero when $\pi \neq 2$, and both equal to 1 when $\pi = 2$.

The Euler characteristic $\chi(K, G) = \sum_p (-1)^p b_p$ is the same for all these groups, for, by the formulae of Theorem 6.5, it is also equal to $\Sigma(-1)^p \alpha_p$.

The following theorem shows that the Betti numbers are the same in the integral and rational cases.

THEOREM 6.6 *The maximum number b_p of integral p-cycles linearly independent with respect to homology is equal in the maximum number b_p^* of rational p-cycles linearly independent with respect to homology.*

Proof. Suppose that the rational p-cycles $c_1^p, \ldots, c_r^p$ are such that, if $u_1, \ldots, u_r$ are rational numbers, $\sum_i u_i c_1^p$ is not a bounding p-cycle unless all the u's are zero. Then, in particular, there is no set of r integral p-cycles such that any linear combination, with integral coefficients not all zero, is a bounding cycle. Thus $b_p \geqq b_p^*$.

Now suppose that the rational p-cycles $c_1^p, \ldots, c_r^p$ are such that there is a rational p-cycle $\gamma^p = \sum_i u_i c_i^p$ which is a non-zero bounding p-cycle. Since the c's are rational p-cycles, their coefficients are of the form u/v where u and v are integers; the coefficients u_i are also of this form. Let k be the least common multiple of all the denominators of the coefficients in the p-cycles and the coefficients u_i. Then $kc_1^p, kc_2^p, \ldots, kc_r^p$ are integral p-cycles such that $\sum_i ku_i c_i^p$ is a bounding integral p-cycle. Therefore $b_p \leqq b_p^*$, and, combining this with the previous result, we have $b_p = b_p^*$.

Theorem 6.6 must not be interpreted as meaning that homology does not distinguish between the rational and integral cases. Though the Betti numbers are the same, the homology groups need not be.

For example, the homology group H^1 for the complex of figure 26 has been shown to be a cyclic group of order two in the integral case and the identity in the rational case.

The distinction is expressed not by the Betti numbers but by the torsion coefficients.

53. Cohomology. If c^p is the p-chain $\Sigma u_i \sigma_i^p$ in a complex K, the coboundary Γc^p is the $(p+1)$-chain $\sum_{i,j} u_i \eta_{ji}^{p+1} \tau_j^{p+1}$. This definition is similar to that of the boundary Δc^p, but the operator Γ raises the dimension by 1, whereas Δ lowers it by 1. The properties of Γ are similar to those of Δ; for example, $\Gamma(\Gamma c^p)$ is zero.

A chain whose coboundary is zero is called a **cocycle**. Every coboundary is a cocycle, but a cocycle need not be a coboundary. The set of cocycles in K forms a subgroup Z_p of C^p, and the set of cobounding cocycles forms a subgroup B_p of Z_p. The difference group $Z_p - B_p$, which consists of cohomology classes of cocycles, is called the pth **cohomology group** of K. The cohomology groups possess similar properties to those of the homology groups. Like the homology groups, the cohomology groups are topological invariants.

54. Calculation of homology groups. Theoretically the homology groups of a triangulable topological space can be calculated by examining the cycles and bounding cycles in any triangulation. But this process is seldom used in practice, because the calculation can be very complicated. A better method is to use **cell complexes** instead of simplicial complexes. A cell complex is similar in nature to a simplicial complex, but consists of cells instead of simplexes. An **open p-cell** is any space homeomorphic with the set $\Sigma_i x_i^2 < 1$ in Euclidean space of p dimensions. Incidence of cells and orientation can be defined by analogy with the simplicial case; however various theoretical difficulties are encountered (see Eilenberg and Steenrod, *Foundations of Algebraic Topology*, page 181, and Steenrod's *The Topology of Fibre Bundles*, page 155). Here we are concerned with the practical value of cell complexes and not with their theory. Thus we do not attempt to justify the methods used in the following examples, which illustrate the use of cell complexes. It is worth mentioning, however, that the homology groups calculated from a cellular decomposition of a space are isomorphic with the homology groups calculated from a simplicial decomposition. This follows from the uniqueness theorem for homology theories for triangulable spaces. (See Eilenberg and Steenrod, loc. cit., Chapter III).

Example 1 (*the torus*). A cellular decomposition of the torus can be obtained from the representation by means of a rectangle with opposite sides identified, as shown in figure 28. In this case there is

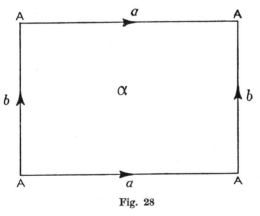

Fig. 28

one 2-cell α whose boundary is $a - b - a + b = 0$, and so α is a 2-cycle. There are no 3-cells, and so α is a non-bounding 2-cycle. If k is any non-zero integer, $k\alpha$ is a non-bounding 2-cycle, and it is not homologous to any other 2-cycle of this form. Moreover these are the only integral 2-cycles, and so the integral homology group H^2 is an infinite cyclic group, and the Betti number $b_2 = 1$. There are two 1-cycles a and b, and they do not bound, since the boundary of the only 2-cell is zero. It follows that the integral homology group H^1 is the direct sum of two infinite cyclic groups, and that the Betti number b_1 is equal to 2. Finally the only 0-cell A is a non-bounding

0-cycle, and it follows that the integral homology group H^0 is an infinite cyclic group and that $b_0 = 1$.

Example 2 (*the real projective plane*). Using the representation shown in figure 29, we have one 2-cell α whose boundary is $2(a + b)$.

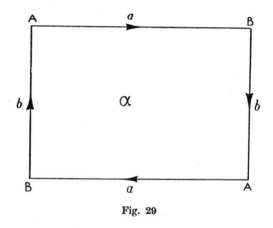

Fig. 29

Thus there are no non-zero 2-cycles, and the integral homology group H^2 is the identity, and $b_2 = 0$. The 1-cell a is not a 1-cycle, because its boundary is $B - A$, but $a + b$ is a 1-cycle. This 1-cycle is not the boundary of a 2-cell; however, $2(a + b)$ is the boundary of α. Therefore the integral homology group H^1 is a cyclic group of order two; also $b_1 = 0$ and there is one non-trivial one-dimensional torsion coefficient equal to 2. Finally the integral homology group H^0 is an infinite cyclic group, since no two 0-cycles of the form kA (where k is an integer) are homologous, but B is homologous to A. The Betti number b_0 is equal to 1.

Example 3 (*the Klein bottle*). This is represented in figure 30. Here the boundary of α is $2b$, and so there are no non-zero 2-cycles; hence H^2 is the identity, and $b_2 = 0$. The 1-cells a and b are both non-bounding 1-cycles; every 1-cycle ka is a non-bounding cycle not homologous to any other 1-cycle of this form, but $2b$ is a bounding 1-cycle, since it is the boundary of α. Hence the integral group H^1 is the direct sum of an infinite cyclic group and a cyclic group of order two. Thus $b_1 = 1$, and there is a non-trivial one-dimensional torsion coefficient equal to 2. Finally, as in the previous case, H^0 is an infinite cyclic group, and $b_0 = 1$.

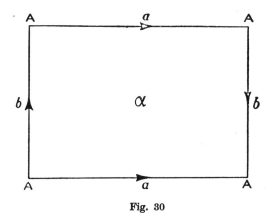

Fig. 30

Exercises.

(1) Use the triangulation obtained in exercise 1 of Chapter V to calculate the integral homology groups and the homology groups modulo a prime π of the Klein bottle.

(2) An orientable closed surface, other than the sphere, can be represented by a polygon of $4p$ sides, identified in such a way that the perimeter is described according to the scheme $a_1 b_1 a_1^{-1} b_1^{-1} \ldots a_p b_p a_p^{-1} b_p^{-1}$, as indicated in figure 31 (see Lefschetz's *Introduction to Topology*, p. 78); this means that the polygon has $2p$ distinct sides $a_1, \ldots, a_p, b_1, \ldots, b_p$ and that, following the perimeter clockwise, we have a_1, followed by b_1, then a_1 reversed, then b_1 reversed and so on. Calculate the integral homology groups, the Betti numbers and the torsion coefficients of the surface, by treating this representation as a cell complex.

(3) A non-orientable closed surface can be represented by a polygon of $2q$ sides, identified in such a way that the perimeter is described according to the scheme $a_1 a_1 a_2 a_2 \ldots a_q a_q$ (Lefschetz, loc. cit.) Calculate the integral homology groups, the Betti numbers and the torsion coefficients of this surface.

(4) A surface S_1 is constructed from the surface of a torus by

removing a simply-connected region. Calculate the integral homology groups of S_1.

(5) A surface S_2 is constructed from the surface of a torus by removing two disjoint simply connected regions. Calculate the integral homology groups of this surface.

(6) Generalise exercises 4 and 5 by calculating the integral homology groups of a surface S_n obtained from a torus by removing n disjoint simply connected regions.

(7) A space T_3 is formed from the disc $x^2 + y^2 \leqq 1$ in the Euclidean plane by identifying points P, P' on the circumference $x^2 + y^2 = 1$ such that the arc PP' subtends an angle $2\pi/3$ or $4\pi/3$ at the centre. Show that the Betti numbers of T_3 are the same as those of the real projective plane, and that there is a non-trivial one-dimensional torsion coefficient equal to 3.

(8) By generalising the space T_3 of exercise 7, construct a space T_n whose Betti numbers are the same as those of the real projective plane, and such that there is a non-trivial one-dimensional torsion coefficient equal to n.

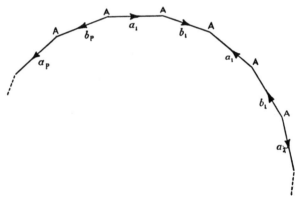

Fig. 31

BIBLIOGRAPHY

BOURBAKI, N., *Topologie Générale*, Paris, 1948.

EILENBERG, S. and STEENROD, N., *Foundations of Algebraic Topology*, Princeton, 1952.

HILTON, P. J., *An Introduction to Homotopy Theory*, Cambridge, 1953.

LEFSCHETZ, S., *Introduction to Topology*, Princeton, 1949.

LEFSCHETZ, S., *Algebraic Topology*, New York, 1942.

NEWMAN, M. H. A., *Elements of the Topology of Plane Sets of Points*, Cambridge, 1951.

PONTRJAGIN, L., *Topological Groups*, Princeton, 1946.

PONTRJAGIN, L., *Foundations of Combinatorial Topology*, Rochester, 1952.

SEIFERT, H. and THRELFALL, W., *Lehrbuch der Topologie*, Leipzig, Teubner, 1934.

SIERPINSKI, W., *General Topology*, Toronto, 1952.

STEENROD, N. E., *Topology of Fibre Bundles*, Princeton, 1951.

VEBLEN, O., *Analysis Situs*, New York, 1931.

INDEX